The Health Services
of Tanganyika

African Medical
and Research Foundation

The Health Services
of Tanganyika
A Report to the Government

Richard M. Titmuss (Chairman)
Brian Abel-Smith, George Macdonald
Arthur W. Williams, Christopher H. Wood

London
Pitman Medical Publishing Co. Ltd.

First published 1964

PITMAN MEDICAL PUBLISHING COMPANY LTD.
46 Charlotte Street, London, W.1

Associated Companies
SIR ISAAC PITMAN AND SONS LTD.
Pitman House, Parker Street, Kingsway,
London, W.C.2
The Pitman Press, Bath
Pitman House, Bouverie Street, Carlton, Melbourne
22-25 Beckett's Buildings, President Street,
Johannesburg

PITMAN PUBLISHING CORPORATION
20 East 46th Street, New York

SIR ISAAC PITMAN AND SONS (CANADA) LTD.
(Incorporating the Commercial Text Book Company)
Pitman House, 381-383 Church Street, Toronto

c C

Printed by Charles Birchall & Sons Ltd.,
Liverpool and London

Contents

The Minister of Health,
P.O. Box 9083,
Dar es Salaam,
TANGANYIKA

Dear Mr. Maswanya,

In July 1961, the African Medical and Research Foundation notified Professor Macdonald, Dr. Williams and myself that Mr. Bryceson, who was then Minister of Health, wished us to undertake a review of the medical services of Tanganyika. The terms of reference for this assignment were as follows:

'To examine the present organization of the medical services in Tanganyika, bearing in mind the desirability of close integration of government and the voluntary agencies health services and to recommend:

1. Ways and means of extending the curative services over the next five years in order to achieve maximum even coverage territorially;

2. How preventive medicine and other means of health education may best be promoted;

3. The staff which will be necessary to put expansion plans into operation;

4. How this staff may be trained locally, bearing in mind that it may not in every case be either necessary or desirable to insist upon United Kingdom qualifications, but that reasonable standards must be maintained; and

5. What proportion of available finance should be devoted to each activity of the health services.'

The Health Services of Tanganyika

We were told that the Government was anxious that the inquiry should start as soon as possible. Unfortunately, we all had prior commitments which prevented us from visiting Tanganyika before the end of 1961. I therefore suggested that a preliminary visit for the purposes of fact-collecting should be made by Dr. Abel-Smith of the London School of Economics and Political Science and Dr. Wood of the London School of Hygiene and Tropical Medicine. This was agreed and they visited Tanganyika for five weeks during August and September, 1961. After a week in Dar es Salaam they made a rapid tour of different parts of the country which was facilitated by the plane placed at their disposal by the Foundation. During their stay in Tanganyika, they visited thirty-one different medical establishments including some owned by the Government, some by missions (voluntary agencies), some by local government, and some by private employers. They estimated that, between them, they had discussions with over a third of the doctors in Tanganyika. In addition, they met formally and informally many members of the nursing and medical auxiliary professions. Informal meetings were held with representatives of both medical associations in Dar es Salaam and elsewhere and with representatives of the Tanganyika Medical Workers' Union.

On their return Doctors Abel-Smith and Wood presented a report of over a hundred pages which summarized the present problems of the health services and reported as impartially as possible the different representations which had been made to them. They also had with them for reference several hundred pages of notes which they had dictated during their stay. In view of this report and the background knowledge they had acquired, I suggested that they should be made full members of the survey committee. This was agreed.

On the basis of this information and the extensive experience of the problems of East Africa of Professor Macdonald and Dr. Williams, the enlarged Committee held regular meetings during the autumn. We took advantage of a visit by Mr. Bryceson to London on other business in November to invite him to meet us—singly and collectively. It was at this stage that we were informed of some of the Government's proposals including licensing fees for private practitioners, which were announced in Parliament a few weeks later. The Committee agreed to continue its work within the context of this new declaration of policy.

Early in 1962 Professor Macdonald spent four weeks travelling extensively throughout Tanganyika visiting hospitals, health centres and dispensaries to assess their qualities and difficulties as a background to our planning of health facilities in rural areas. He also participated in the discussion of proposals to establish a new course of training for medical practitioners at Dar es Salaam. On his return he communicated this proposal to the other members of the Committee and we expressed some preliminary views on this subject in the early summer of 1962 as we understood that it was hoped to start the course that year (the start of the course has since been postponed to 1963). This particular subject is discussed in Chapter 9 of our report.

Further meetings of the Committee were held throughout the summer but it was not until August and September, 1962 that it was possible for the whole Committee to visit Tanganyika. We did not consider it necessary to ask for formal evidence to be submitted to us. On the other hand, we took steps to have discussions with all those principally concerned, and to seek advice in as many quarters as possible. Thus, we met representatives of the professional organizations, all of whom helped us in our work. In particular, we would like to stress the value which we attached to evidence given us by a representative of the Tanganyika Medical Workers' Union who presented us with an organizational chart indicating how the health services should, in the view of his Union, be reorganized.

Though we made contact with leading doctors in voluntary agencies of many denominations and had talks with several bishops, it was not possible to arrange a meeting of the Mission Medical Advisory Committee to coincide with our visit. Moreover, the secretary of the Committee was not in Dar es Salaam while we were all assembled there.

We regret this omission. Nevertheless, we managed to meet three members of the Committee on an individual basis, and learnt about the submissions that had been made to the government.

During our stay in Tanganyika members of the Committee made visits to several different parts of the country. In particular, visits were arranged to Ifakara to see Professor Geigy's unit, to Dodoma to study at first hand the working of the health and other services in the area, and to Mwanza.

The Committee was fortunate in being able to make use of the voluntary services of Mrs. Rosemary Stevens of the Yale Department of Epidemiology and Public Health who happened to be in Tanganyika before and during this visit. She was engaged upon work which was closely related to our own study and kindly undertook on our behalf research into the historical development of the health services. Chapter 1 is almost wholly based upon her work. She also assembled the major part of the information upon which Chapter 2 is based. After our return from Tanganyika she attended most of our meetings in London. The accuracy and thoroughness of the background material is largely due to her careful research work.

In preparing our report we wished to take account of recent plans and proposals in other countries at similar levels of development. With this aim in mind, several members of the Committee visited hospitals and health centres in Kenya and Uganda and had talks with the staff of the Ministries of Health and the University of East Africa. Dr. Williams also attended the East African Director of Medical Services' Conference held in Nairobi in September. We would like to acknowledge all the help that was given us. We have also been in close touch with the World Health Organization both in Geneva and in Brazzaville. We have also studied a number of reports[1] which have been of assistance to us in seeing the problems of Tanganyika in broader perspective.

---

[1] Federation of Rhodesia and Nyasaland, *Report of the Commission of Inquiry into the Health and Medical Services of the Federation*, Salisbury, 1959: World Health Organization, *Second Report on the World Health Situation* (*1957-60*):

Letter of Transmittal

As a small Committee, it has been possible for much of the discussion and drafting to be done by informal contacts between two or more members. Any statistics about formal meetings which we have held since our appointment would, therefore, give a wholly misleading impression of the amount of work which this report has entailed. At one stage in our deliberations each member of the Committee took responsibility for preparing drafts on particular aspects of the study and discussed separate points with other members. All these drafts were subsequently discussed by the whole Committee at numerous meetings in London.

We have interpreted our terms of reference somewhat widely. The phrase 'medical services' is sometimes used internationally in a sense which is confined to services for diagnosis and treatment and sometimes in a broader sense to cover all health services. We have made use of this wider interpretation. We also found it necessary to take account of many other factors affecting health and disease, and which involve relationships between health agencies and other agencies concerned with the objective of raising levels of living.

We were asked to produce a plan for extending the ser-

Kaser, C. *Health Planning as part of the national development plan*, WHO, Geneva, 1960:

Manuwa, S. 'The principles and methodology of planning the Development of National Health Programmes in Underdeveloped Countries' *West African Medical Journal*, April, 1961:

Kershaw, J. D. *A Study of the Health Services in Kenya* (Unpublished):

Report of the Commission of Enquiry into the Health Needs of the Gold Coast, Gold Coast, 1952:

Black, S. *Health Services in the Congo Republic* WHO, Geneva, 1961:

Seshageri Rau, S. *Problems in Planning Health Services in India*, WHO, Geneva, 1960:

World Health Organization, *Planning of Public Health Services*, Geneva, 1961:

Statement by the Protectorate Government on the Reimposition of Charges for Medical Treatment in Government Medical Units, Entebbe, 1952.

Spens, Teresa. *Report on Home Economics in Africa*, FAO, Rome, 1962:

Food and Agriculture Organization, *Report on the Possibilities of African Rural Development in Relation to Economic and Social Growth*, Rome, 1962.

Selwyn-Clarke, S. *Report on a Programme for the Health Services in Ghana*, Accra, 1961.

vices over a five-year period. In a letter we sent to your predecessor in July 1962, we explained that we thought it would be more helpful to look further ahead. The forces of population growth; the rate of economic and educational advance; the time that is required to start new training programmes and for qualified men and women to be trained in substantial numbers; all these and other factors, which we trust are made clear in our report, demand a longer view than five years.

We decided, therefore, to think broadly in terms of a twenty-year period of development. Occasionally, we have cited the year 1980. This may imply a degree of precision which we would ask you and your advisers not to take too seriously. We have not attempted to produce a blue print for this or any other year. The 'expert' has his limitations; he is after all only a servant, and should always remember how little he really knows. What we have tried to do, therefore, within these limitations, is to recommend stages of development over the next two decades, and to show how progress in one sector depends on progress in other sectors. The pace of development in the health field is, however, largely a question of political priorities upon which we can offer little guidance.

The Chief Medical Officer and his staff have given fully and generously of their time, knowledge and experience. No information has been held back from us. No questions have gone unanswered. We were allowed access to confidential files, statistical records and other data with a freedom which made us feel like members of the department rather than investigators of its work. We are very conscious of the disruption of normal work which is caused by the invasion of a Committee such as ours. We wish, therefore, to thank all the members of the Medical Department and other government departments to whom we turned for help for everything they did, formally and informally, to aid us in our work.

The completion of this report has been greatly facilitated by excellent secretarial services provided at different stages of our work. Miss Sheila Benson carried the main burden of the work for the first year, Mrs. Davey while we were in Tanganyika, and Miss Pamela Morgan and Miss Elizabeth Thomas for the final stages in London. Mr. Tony Lynes and Mrs. Angela Vivian also contributed in the final stages in various ways. To all of them we owe special thanks not only for accurate work in the day but also for week-end work and night work which speeded the preparation of the report.

This letter would not be complete without acknowledgment of all the help provided by the African Medical and Research Foundation. Not only have they allowed us to incur any expenditure which we regarded as necessary for undertaking the survey, but they also made arrangements for our visits to Tanganyika, provided secretarial services for us, and undertook other administrative tasks on our behalf. Finally, while paying for the cost of the whole survey from our appointment to the production of the report, they accepted without question the principle that our loyalty and responsibility was exclusively to you and your predecessors.

Yours sincerely,

Richard M. Titmuss (*Chairman*)

on behalf of the Medical Survey Committee—

Brian Abel-Smith
George Macdonald
Arthur W. Williams
Christopher H. Wood

London, January, 1963.

1 Development of
the Health Services of Tanganyika

Western medicine was first brought to Tanganyika by the missionaries. In 1877 the Church Missionary Society, stimulated by Livingstone, opened the first hospital at Mamboia. They were followed by many other missionary societies, both from Britain and Germany, who settled and taught in Tanganyika in the second half of the nineteenth century. But outside a very small circle these early endeavours by voluntary agencies made little impression on the health or health practices of the African population. The history of organized medical services properly begins in 1888 with the period of German administration.

In 1891 the Germans set up a medical department to supervise the health of government employees. The initial staff of the department included five medical officers and fourteen German medical orderlies. The years that followed were turbulent ones, characterized by local uprisings and widespread epidemics and dogged by sickness. Following the failure of the Maji Maji rebellion in 1905 there was a brief span of comparative quiet before the outbreak of the First World War which was to end German rule. But during the twenty-six years of this administration, the Germans laid the foundations of a hospital system which was to be developed during the more tranquil years of British administration after 1918. They built some twelve general hospitals, the largest of which was a hospital of seventy-five beds at Tabora. They established a sanatorium in the Usambara Mountains,

I

a 'lunatic asylum' at Lutindi, and provided leprosy segregation camps for over three thousand patients.

The Germans also made an important start with public health services. In 1897/98 a Government laboratory was established in Dar es Salaam. This was visited by Dr. Robert Koch on several occasions while he was working on malaria and other endemic diseases. Calf lymph for vaccination against smallpox and quinine for the mass treatment of malaria were produced locally and campaigns were launched against plague and sleeping sickness. By 1914, there were sixty-three doctors in the country, ten of whom were working in mission stations or practising privately. Of the fifty-three who were working for the government medical department nine were engaged solely on the sleeping sickness programme—one-seventh of the country's total medical strength.

On the outbreak of the First World War, all available staff were mobilized and the civil medical services were taken over by the German Army. When the campaign began in East Africa, many diseases wrought havoc among both German and British allied troops. By the beginning of 1917, 80% of the 15,000 troops brought up by the British from South Africa had to be evacuated because of malaria. African porters and subordinates on both sides suffered particularly heavily from disease.

The Years of Expansion, 1919-1929
At the end of the war, the civilian medical services were in a neglected state. They were taken over first by the British Army, then gradually by a British Civil Medical Service. The transfer was completed in 1919. The new medical department inherited about 1,200 hospital beds, of which eighty-six were for mental patients, and an urban public health service which had deteriorated greatly during the war years.

The department was organized in two separate branches: the medical branch took over responsibility for the hospitals and the sanitation branch assumed responsibility for most of the public health work. In practice, the work of the latter was concentrated almost entirely in the larger towns where the majority of the expatriate population had settled. Out of the sanitation budget of £22,600 for 1921/22, over a third was spent in the capital city of Dar es Salaam. Immediate steps were taken in this and other towns to improve water supplies and waste disposal services and to attack mosquito breeding grounds. But not until 1928 did the sanitation branch report that 'the sanitation of towns might be regarded as satisfactory'.[1]

The sanitation branch was supervised by a doctor with public health qualifications and two other doctors were assigned as Medical Officers of Health for Dar es Salaam and Tanga. Seven European sanitary superintendents completed the branch's complement of trained staff, which supervised the work of over seven hundred African subordinates and labourers. The sanitation branch was allocated 23% of the medical department vote in 1920/21, and over 21% a year later. Public health work was not, however, confined to this branch. Although the principle was early expressed that 'better sanitary work will be done by officers who are assured against liability to recall to ordinary medical duties',[2] it was not intended to isolate the preventive from the curative aspects of medicine: only in the large towns were these two functions separately administered. In 1922, out of the seventeen medical practitioners engaged in executive duties, two were wholly engaged in public health work and all the others were responsible for both medical and sanitary work in the twenty-two districts and nineteen sub-districts of the country.

A number of Africans had gained experience of medical work and field hygiene during the war. These included members of a 'Mosquito Brigade' set up by the British Army to discover and deal with mosquito breeding grounds. Otherwise there were very few trained or even slightly experienced Africans, especially for public health work. In an attempt to remedy this defect a course was started to train urban sanitary inspectors in Dar es Salaam in 1921. Lessons were

1 *Annual Report of the Medical Department*, 1928, p. 36.
2 *Annual Report of the Medical Department*, 1922, p. 27.

3

given in elementary hygiene, public health and sanitary engineering by the city's medical officer of health, assisted by two sanitary superintendents. In 1924, it was found possible to introduce a more formal twelve-month course in English instead of Swahili. The medical officer of health of Dar es Salaam also started a school health service. From 1921 he and a sub-assistant surgeon paid weekly visits to the government school and arrangements were made for the government's one dental surgeon to make periodic school dental inspections. School medical services were to remain confined to the capital. Some forty years later it was reported that it had still not 'been found possible to provide a formal school health service anywhere outside Dar es Salaam'.[3]

The sanitation branch was responsible from the start for communicable disease campaigns. The anti-malaria programmes were fortified in the mid-twenties by the appointment of an entomologist and later by the formation of two malaria units. Sleeping sickness programmes, despite the early enthusiasm of the Germans, were slow to develop. It was not until 1925, when the Rhodesian form of the disease had appeared and three new foci had been discovered, that a sleeping sickness unit was formed. By then, the Government employed forty-five doctors and forty Asian assistant and sub-assistant surgeons.[4] By 1928, seventy-two staff were specifically assigned to the sleeping sickness unit, including six doctors, two sub-assistant surgeons, eleven compounders and dispensers and four agricultural surveyors. In addition, ten other professional staff performed part-time sleeping sickness duties. Despite all this effort, sleeping sickness remained a serious health hazard in many areas.

In 1927, a special epidemiological investigation was undertaken among the African population in the Kahama district by a team which included a medical officer, four sub-assistant surgeons and two nursing sisters and health visitors. The purpose of the project was to establish reliable

---

[3] *Annual Report of the Medical Department*, 1960, p. 13.
[4] Assistant or sub-assistant surgeons and compounders were recruited from India. The former were doctors whose qualifications were not registrable in the United Kingdom. In Tanganyika they were licensed to practise in approved (usually government) posts.

statistics, to investigate social and cultural patterns relating to health, and to conduct general medical and maternal and child health work. Although valuable statistical and descriptive information was collected, the project had to be abruptly abandoned in 1931 after an epidemic of sleeping sickness had swept through the district. No similar project on this scale has been carried out since.

The outstanding medical campaign of the twenties was an extensive and spectacular attack on individual cases of yaws. After the discovery of bismuth treatment more and more cases were identified and treated each year. The numbers treated rose from 1,100 in 1921 to 75,700 in 1925 and 126,400 in 1929.[5]

The demand for this service grew rapidly. By the end of 1925 fifty-five stationary and mobile treatment centres had been set up, and many more were added by 1929. By this time the number of patients coming forward for treatment was beginning to fall off. More than half a million people, or one-ninth of the estimated population, had by then, however, been treated for yaws and over 100,000 for syphilis. The campaign had demonstrated vividly to the rural population the effectiveness of western medicine. This was to have important and lasting consequences for the future of the health services, particularly in creating demand for curative treatment.

Both the budget and the staff of the medical department had been increasing throughout the twenties. Government expenditure on health services rose from £79,000 in 1921 to over £252,000 in 1929. The number of doctors rose from twenty-two in 1921 to fifty-nine in 1929; the number of sub-assistant surgeons from twenty-one to sixty-six, the number of compounders from twenty-five to thirty-six and the number of European nursing staff from seventeen to forty-seven. By 1929, the department also employed two dental surgeons, a bacteriologist, an entomologist and an analytical chemist. Over these years the department steadily developed from a small medical unit whose primary purpose was to safeguard the health of Government employees and their

---

[5] *Annual Reports of the Medical Department*, 1921/29.

families to an organization responsible for the whole population.

From the mid-twenties on it was recognized that as the country could not possibly afford to employ a sufficient number of trained expatriate staff, auxiliary medical grades with specific functions would have to be trained. Three grades were established; African district sanitary inspector, dispenser and tribal dresser. The first of these gradually evolved through improvements in recruitment and training until in 1952 the grade of assistant health inspector was created; in 1962 a training course for full health inspectors was started. The second grade developed with further training into a hospital assistant in the 1930s and 1940s and a medical assistant in the 1950s. The third category, that of the tribal dresser, remains today; although here too the upgrading process can be seen in the development of a separate and higher grade of rural medical aid.

Training for district sanitary inspectors started in 1925. The course consisted of three months of practical instruction in the health office at Dar es Salaam, Tanga or Tabora. Applicants had to be literate in Swahili but no other educational standards were demanded. Because of the educative purpose of the new inspectors, an attempt was made to select for training people with some standing in the community, so that their advice would carry weight when they returned to their own district. 'It is essential,' wrote Shircore, 'that the African district sanitary inspectors shall be fully acquainted with the prejudices of the people amongst whom they have to work. The African villager is one of the most conservative persons in the world and little or nothing will be accomplished by sending an alien inspector, however well trained, to alter the habits of centuries.'[6]

Whereas the urban sanitary inspector worked directly under a doctor or sanitary superintendent, the district inspector worked on his own, though he had to submit monthly reports to the district medical officer. In 1929 eleven district sanitary inspectors working in the Dar es Salaam district were responsible for supervising some 35,000 huts with

---

[6] *Annual Report of the Medical Department*, 1925, p. 36.

a population of over 100,000. At the same time there were 218 trained district sanitary inspectors deployed in the rural areas. The *Annual Report of the Medical Department for 1928* gave two examples of how district inspectors reported an outbreak of bubonic plague and 'independently undertook the necessary preventive measures'. It was said that 'the African district sanitary inspector fulfils an essential function, and forms an important and valuable intelligence liaison between the endemic and epidemic fields in the districts and the central administration, which could not be attained, with certainty and regularity, in any other way'.[7]

The training for African 'dispensers' was at a much higher level and was designed primarily for the curative services. Dispensers were originally recruited from Nyasaland to work in small stationary dispensaries, or in travelling clinics to look after the workers employed on road construction, and they were a vital factor in the campaign against yaws. The course which was started in Tanganyika in the middle twenties consisted of eighteen months divided between the Medical Training School at the Sewa Haji Hospital in Dar es Salaam and the larger district hospitals. The curriculum included elementary anatomy and physiology, the elements of medicine, minor surgery and first aid, together with a brief period of tuition in welfare work, practical village sanitation and elementary dental practice. It was hoped to turn out sufficient qualified students to maintain a complement of 250 dispensers, or one to every 20,000 population—a target that has yet to be achieved. By the end of 1929, eighty-one dispensers had been trained. They were employed as hospital assistants in the larger hospitals and some of the more experienced were put in sole charge of government dispensaries. Those in independent charge of dispensaries treated over 40,000 cases in 1929. In that year the number of government in-patient and out-patient cases had tripled from 11,700 in-patients in 1921 to 34,800, and from 100,700 out-patients in 1921 to 361,100 in 1929.

The grade of tribal dresser was created in response to the

---

[7] *Annual Report of the Medical Department*, 1928, p. 9.

demand of native authorities for rural medical treatment services.

> ... The tribal dressers are selected by their chiefs from amongst the more intelligent members of their tribe, and undergo a three months training by the regular medical staff in the uses of scheduled drugs and equipment, and have the pamphlet of instructions, which is printed in English and Kiswahili, issued to them for reference. They are also given an elementary course of practical sanitation as relating to housing, protection of food and water supplies, the destruction of refuse, the disposal of excreta and the destruction of animal and insect pests. . . .[8]

Despite the public health content of this training, the native authority dispensaries which developed rapidly in the late twenties became—and remained—first aid and treatment centres. The grade was an immediate success. By the end of 1929 dressers were staffing 247 native authority dispensaries and 190,500 cases were treated in that year. Gradually the tribal dispensaries became the largest first-line medical service in the country. It was estimated 'with some confidence' in 1929 that the full complement of 1,000 rural dispensaries would be set up within the next four to five years. It was, however, many years before this target was achieved.

The work of the medical department in the twenties was not limited to hospital and dispensary treatment and environmental health services. In 1924 a nursing sister was assigned to establish a maternal and child welfare clinic in Dar es Salaam. A further clinic was opened in the following year under a health visitor at Tabora. At the end of 1929, the Government was employing eleven fully trained health visitors for maternal and child welfare work. In that year over 43,000 mothers and children were seen in government clinics. The Missions had also begun to make a substantial contribution in this field; a further 25,000 cases were seen in their clinics in 1929.

Early in the twenties an attempt had been made to isolate compulsorily patients suffering from leprosy. Within a few

---

[8] *Annual Report of the Medical Department*, 1926, p. 10.

years, this policy had to be abandoned chiefly because it proved impossible to carry out. In 1929 there were about 3,500 leprosy patients in forty-four centres or settlements scattered throughout Tanganyika : there remained an unknown number who had not come forward for treatment. Changes were also made in the mental hospital field. 'Lunatics' and 'lunatic asylums' became 'patients' and 'mental hospitals', although this was not enforced by legislation until 1941. In 1929, there were two mental hospitals, one at Dodoma and the other at Lutindi, with a total of 170 beds.

Financial Retrenchment 1930-1938

The world slump halted and reversed the progress achieved in many of these fields during the 1920s. The effects on the Tanganyikan economy were severe and lasted for over a decade. In 1930, Government medical expenditure reached £274,715 but this was followed by immediate financial retrenchment and it was not until 1943 that the expenditure level of 1930 was regained. By 1936 expenditure had fallen by about a third to £186,000, and the figure was not much higher in 1939. In 1938 there was an establishment of forty-seven Government doctors compared with fifty-nine in 1929. New projects were abandoned, staff were not appointed to vacant posts and hospital maintenance costs were cut.[9] Training schemes were not developed at the expected rate and plans for the upgrading of staff in the rural services were not fulfilled. By 1934 there were only twenty-nine Government doctors in executive medical and health posts, which meant that there was only one to 173,000 population. In the rural areas, the number of African district sanitary inspectors was reduced from 218 in 1929 to 140 in 1931 : a reduction that has continued to this day.

---

[9] Special research undertaken with the assistance of the Colonial Development Fund was not, however, affected. This included the research laboratory for tuberculosis established at Moshi in 1930 which continued its work until 1937. The malaria research unit at Dar es Salaam which was set up in 1931 continued its work until 1938. Sleeping sickness research, which had begun at Tinde in 1926, was also brought under the Colonial Development Fund in 1934. Approximately £7,000 was provided for medical research from the Fund in 1938.

The preventive services—and all the hopeful plans for their development—were the major victims of the depression. The curative services, on the other hand, continued to expand throughout the thirties though at a considerably slower rate than in the 1920s. By 1939, more cases were seen by tribal dressers in local authority dispensaries than in central government out-patient and in-patient departments put together. The relative development of the Central Government and Local Authority services is shown in Table I.

Table I

The Development of Public Medical Services 1921/1941

Year	Central Government		Local Authority	
	Number of cases seen (Thousands)		Number of cases seen (Thousands)	Number of rural dispensaries
	In-patients	Out-patients	Out-patients	
1921	12	101	—	—
1926	27	308	Not recorded	35
1931	33	423	370	285
1936	38	598	530	297
1941	45	863	1,113	314

Although the period was one of retrenchment there were, however, some important changes and developments in staff training during the 1930s. In 1936, the course for dispensers (later medical assistants) was extended to three years and candidates were required to possess Standard X education —a requirement which remained until the course was abolished in 1962. The decision was also taken to start training at a higher level African staff to man the rural medical services. It was felt that the three-month training course for tribal dressers was inadequate. The country's educational system was now producing more candidates with better education than had been required for tribal dressers. Accordingly, an eighteen-month course for 'medical auxiliaries' (later rural medical aids) was set up in 1935, in a specially built training centre at Mwanza which is still the main government training centre for this purpose. The course was basically the same as that given to tribal dressers but at a more advanced level. Particular emphasis was laid on the routine examination of patients, on the technique of injections and on the diagnosis of common African diseases with the use of a microscope. Thus 'The microscope and the syringe became field weapons in the struggle against helminthic and protozoal diseases.'[10] It was hoped that these new medical auxiliaries would be capable of recognizing and treating common diseases and also of gauging the significance of common clinical signs and symptoms, so that serious cases could be sent on to a district or mission hospital without delay. Similar courses, but on a smaller scale, were set up by the native authorities at Bukoba and Musoma but did not last for many years. Medical auxiliaries were required to have Standard V education and were taught in Swahili while the dispensers (with ten years of education behind them) were taught in English. By the end of 1938, fifty-one medical auxiliaries had qualified.

Thus, from the late thirties there were three grades of locally trained staff for rural treatment services: the dispensers (later medical assistants) working in Central Government hospitals and dispensaries, the medical auxiliaries (later rural medical aids) and the tribal dressers, the latter continuing to gain some experience in the old three-month *ad hoc* courses at district hospitals.

The training of African laboratory assistants was also begun in the thirties, under the senior pathologist in Dar es Salaam. Formal courses for dispenser students were given in chemistry, physics and pathology in conjunction with the Sewa Haji Hospital training school. By the end of 1938,

[10] *Annual Report of the Medical Department*, 1936, p. 59.

trained Africans were in charge of two of the Territorial laboratory service's branch laboratories and another twenty-eight laboratory-trained dispensers were employed at seventeen hospitals.

The first Tanganyikans to take a full medical course in Africa went to Makerere College in the late 1930s. But only ten Tanganyikan doctors had qualified from Makerere by the end of 1952 and only fourteen were in Government service by the end of 1960—twenty years after the first Tanganyikan student had qualified.

Throughout the thirties the need for stringent economy coupled with the rising demand for curative services curtailed developments in the preventive and public health field. The upgrading of medical auxiliary staff was aimed mainly at improving standards of diagnosis and treatment, rather than developing the public health services. Nevertheless, a more integrated approach to the services as a whole was being advocated before the Second World War. 'The dispensary must become a health centre,' wrote the Director of Medical Services in 1938.

> The preventive outlook must at all costs be inculcated into the dispenser and dresser, although his first duties are curative; and he and the district sanitary inspector should be encouraged to work together and to try to keep their people well, instead of using all the resources of the dispensary to cure the sick.[11]

It was not, however, until the 1950s that a health centre was actually established.

By the outbreak of war, the Medical Department had created the essential foundations of a medical service for Tanganyika. The Department was organized in four broad divisions: the administrative division, dealing with staff, supply and financial matters; the medical and dental division responsible for curative services and the training of personnel; the public health division, which included maternal and child welfare, school health, health of the labour force, nutrition and education programmes, and communic-

---

[11] *Memorandum of Medical Policy*, Dar es Salaam, 1938, p. 8.

able disease control; and the laboratory and research division, divided into pathological, chemical and entomological sections.

The Second World War 1939-1945

The Second World War broke out just as the economy of the country was beginning to recover from the effects of the slump. Although there was no fighting in Tanganyika the war restricted the work of the Medical Department and of the health services in various ways. A number of German doctors were interned at the outbreak of war and eleven of the Government's British medical staff left to join the armed forces. In 1942 the Government had available for duty a total of only thirty-nine doctors for all its functions, which now included health services for the forces, supervision of the health of some thousands of internees and refugees, and the examination of army and labour recruits. Inevitably the staff and facilities of the civilian medical services were reduced but the number of patients attending continued to rise. Over two million cases were seen at the sixty Government hospitals and dispensaries and 314 tribal dispensaries in 1941. In 1945, 2·4 million cases were seen out of a total population estimated to be about five and a half million people. As the Chief Medical Officer wrote frankly in 1942 'preventive work and special campaigns have had to suffer'.[12]

About a quarter of a million African recruits were examined by the Medical Department during the war. This threw an almost intolerable strain on the staff of the services, but produced some illuminating information on the physique of the general population. Out of one illustrative batch of 4,000 recruits one-third were pronounced unfit, and of the two-thirds passed only one-half were fit for active duty.

In 1942 the Government appointed a medical officer exclusively for the health of labour, whose duty it was to advise employers on promoting the health of their workers and to make recommendations to the Labour Board. In addition a dietician was appointed to advise Government hospitals

[12] *An Outline of Post-War Development Proposals*, Dar es Salaam, 1944, p. 41.

and other institutions on adequate nutrition : a medical officer exclusively for nutrition duties was not appointed until
1959.

The training of existing grades of staff continued slowly
during the war. There were also some new developments. A
three-year course in chemical analysis was begun in 1940
and the senior pharmacist started courses for pharmacy assistants. Finally, the training of nurses and midwives was begun; the first African woman nurse to hold the Government
Nursing Certificate qualified in 1943.

Post-War Developments 1946-1955

The government medical services emerged from the
war with a new director and an expanding budget and staff.
Expenditure in 1945 was almost twice that of 1940—
£364,300 as against £193,300. Some part of this increase
was, however, attributable to a rise in salaries and prices.
The Government employed fifty-nine registered and forty-
three licensed medical practitioners and provided 4,300 hospital and dispensary beds, 300 of which were for mental
patients. Missions, industry and the private sector accounted
for a further 2,500 beds and fifty-six doctors. The new Director identified the major fault of the existing services as a
shortage of provision on the public health front.

> ... Our medical service at present cannot be considered
> to be more than a token service. Within the framework
> has been included a health service even more diminutive
> than that qualification implies. If the modern concept of
> public health is to be accepted as comprising the guiding
> and advisory purposes of preventive medicine con-
> cerned with urban, rural and labour health problems, we
> must face the issue of providing an adequately manned
> health service considerably in excess of our present ab-
> surdly small branch of the department.[13]

The economic situation had improved as a result of the
rise in the price of primary products during and after the

---

[13] A Ten-year Development and Welfare Plan for Tanganyika Territory, Dar es
Salaam, 1946, p. 49.

war. A plan for the health services, made in 1947,[14] reflected the general optimism of the times. It was envisaged that over the next twenty years 2,000 medical practitioners and 44,000 hospital beds would need to be provided at a capital cost of £17·6 million and recurrent expenditure increasing to £3·3 million. Fifteen years later there were only about 400 doctors and 19,000 beds in hospitals and dispensaries combined, of which 140 doctors and 7,000 beds were the responsibility of the central government.

By 1948, a variety of medical auxiliary careers were open to Africans. Students with Standard XII education could apply for admission to Makerere College for courses leading to the grade of assistant medical officer. Students with Standard X education could apply for the hospital assistant (earlier 'dispenser') course at the Sewa Haji Hospital training school. The duties of the hospital assistant were to help

> the medical officer in a hospital. He may be asked to treat African out-patients, assist the medical officer at operations, mix medicines, look after the work of the African nursing staff, or take charge of the sick people in the hospital when the medical officer is on safari. Sometimes he has charge of a small dispensary where he does everything himself . . .[15]

Alternatively, the Standard X student could take the first part of the hospital assistant course and then branch out to become a dental or a physiotherapy assistant. Courses were also available to Standard X boys for training as laboratory assistants or medical stores assistants and to Standard VIII boys as medical auxiliaries. Those with Standard VIII education could apply for work as nursing auxiliaries and those with Standard VI as hospital orderlies.

The number of rural dispensaries had by now multiplied into a scattered and un-coordinated network which government medical officers could not hope to supervise effectively

---

[14] Post-War Development—Medical Department, Dar es Salaam, 1947.
[15] Careers for Africans—Unpublished Pamphlet—Medical Department, Dar es Salaam, 1948.

and for which sufficient numbers of qualified staff were not available. There were 334 native authority dispensaries in 1946, compared with 295 in 1939; 1·4 million new cases were seen in 1946, compared with 800,000 in 1939. The quality of treatment given at the dispensaries varied very widely. There were some clinics staffed by trained auxiliaries who were supplied with suitable equipment and a fairly wide range of medicines. At other clinics simple drugs and elementary first-aid were provided by tribal dressers who at the most had only a few months instruction and experience at district hospitals.

The number of trained staff was far less than was required. A maximum of forty student hospital assistants could be accommodated for the three-year course at the training school at Dar es Salaam and only twenty-four students for the two-year medical auxiliary course at Mwanza. In the latter case it was not possible to raise the level of entry above Standard VIII education because of the shortage of candidates with ten years of schooling. Between its formation in 1935 and 1948, 115 students were trained at Mwanza—less than ten a year. A Rural Medical Services Committee, reporting in 1948, suggested that dispensaries should be divided into two grades, those within the effective range of supervision by a doctor and those outside this range, and that the former should be staffed with more highly skilled attendants while the latter remained simply as first-aid posts. This proposal was rejected on the grounds that all dispensaries should be supervised by medical staff; no workable alternative was, however, found.

It was hoped that the mission medical services would gradually become more closely integrated with central and local government rural services. Since the 1920s the work of the missions had been assisted by the government with gifts of drugs and equipment and had been reimbursed by the fees of government patients. The missions had taken an active part in the yaws campaign and participated in other specific disease campaigns, such as ankylostomiasis, leprosy and sleeping sickness. In 1945, missionary societies employed seventeen doctors and provided over 2,000 beds in hospitals and dispensaries, although not all of these were staffed by doctors. Thus, the missions provided approximately a third of the beds in the country. They also supplied at that time the largest maternal and child welfare service. Finally, they contributed substantially to the number of trained staff through their own training programmes—particularly for nurses.

After the war a committee was set up to consider future government policy for aid to missions. Subsequently, regulations were laid down whereby government grants would be paid. It was decided that grants would only be paid to those mission stations with resident medical practitioners and that all payments were at the discretion of the Director of Medical Services who would be advised by a Medical Grants-in-Aid Advisory Committee. Aid would consist both of supplies in kind and cash. Grants for hospitals and other medical work were to be assessed on the number of qualified medical and nursing staff employed. Training grants were to be given for each student passing the appropriate government qualifying examination. In 1949, the Government paid £1,620 to missions in respect of training and £37,253 in respect of hospital grants.

In revised regulations introduced in 1955 a third category of grant was added, based on the extent to which missions were carrying out functions which the government accepted as its own responsibility. These were termed 'additional' grants, payable according to the number of approved beds in voluntary hospitals. Expenditure under these regulations is shown in Table II.

Grants for the maintenance of leprosy and mental patients are not included in these figures, nor the cash value of drugs supplied free to leprosy patients. For many years missions had also been enabled to buy drugs and equipment through the government stores.

In 1949 a review of the medical policy of Tanganyika was undertaken by Dr. (later Sir Eric) Pridie, who was the Chief Medical Adviser to the Colonial Office. The recommendations made on the basis of this review were adopted

Table II

Government Cash Grants to Missions 1938-1961

Year	Expenditure
	£
1938	550
1941	578
1946	5,809
1951	54,776
1956/7	106,129
1961/2	152,000 (estimated)

by the Government.[16] Dr. Pridie accepted as a first principle that there was no alternative but to continue to concentrate resources on curative services:

> ... Although preventive and social medicine have more lasting beneficial effects, it is essential under African conditions to have a well-balanced medical service as curative medicine is demanded by the people and its popularity makes preventive medicine acceptable to them. Full use should be made of existing non-Government organizations to achieve these aims, but the Director of Medical Services must co-ordinate all medical and health activities in the Territory and exercise general supervision. ...

But he advocated that dispensaries should gradually be developed into health centres:

> The Government and Native Administration Dispensaries must work as one organization integrated into the medical service under the direct supervision of the Director and his staff, and should develop into rural health centres

---

[16] Legislative Council of Tanganyika, *A Review of the Medical Policy of Tanganyika*, Dar es Salaam, 1949.

with a preventive medicine bias, and the centres of medical intelligence covering the whole country effectively.

He emphasized that existing facilities should be improved before embarking on ambitious schemes.

Dr. Pridie stressed the inadequacy of the training programmes. At the time of his visit there were only twelve female nurses under training in Government schemes and no midwives or subordinate sanitary officials were being trained. He recommended that many more Africans should be trained for every grade. The maximum number of Tanganyikan doctors should be trained at Makerere College and given responsible posts. A school of hygiene should be established in Dar es Salaam to train public health staff, and a health education centre should be set up. The training of nurses should be extended and a school of midwives should be started to train about thirty midwives a year for the rural areas. The training schemes for medical assistants and rural medical aids should be assimilated at one common standard. The training of all other African assistants should be greatly expedited. Since these long-term training measures would not solve the immediate lack of fully-trained doctors and nurses (at the time of Dr. Pridie's visit there were twenty vacancies in an establishment of forty-nine medical officers) he recommended a substantial increase in British medical staff—an increase which he claimed could be effected within two years if recruitment were started immediately.

He also proposed that the Director of Medical Services should have at headquarters two Deputy Directors, one primarily responsible for social and preventive medicine, the other for clinical and hospital services. There were to be eight Assistant Directors, each of whom, with a senior medical officer as his deputy, would be responsible for a decentralized system of medical services in the provinces. Including the headquarter and provincial medical staff, there was to be a revised establishment of 124 general and special duty officers and fifteen specialists. These recommendations would have increased the number of registered doctors in government service from sixty-two (at December 31st 1949) to 139. No recommendations were made covering the role of assistant and sub-assistant surgeons and East African medical officers, of whom there was a combined total of sixty-three at the end of 1949.

The report further recommended an increase in the number of European nursing sisters, the aim being to employ two sisters at every hospital where there was a registered doctor. The number of sisters and health visitors employed at the end of 1949 was sixty-four: this was to be increased to about 150.

A target of one hospital bed to one thousand population was recommended. This meant an increase from 3,900 to at least 7,000 beds: the new total was to include a new hospital with 400 beds at Dar es Salaam. Finally, Dr. Pridie suggested that all patients, other than the indigent, should pay for treatment on a standard scale used by both government and local authorities. This proposal as well as the rest of the report was accepted as the policy of the government. No estimates were shown of the cost of the plan; nor were time limits set for the proposed developments. The Pridie report was intended to set the pattern of long-term medical policy to be implemented as soon as possible.

In the following five years (1950-1955), efforts were made by the Medical Department to carry out Dr. Pridie's proposals, but serious shortages of staff continued. Nevertheless, the programme for expanding the curative services went ahead. The number of beds in government hospitals and dispensaries rose from 4,535 in 1950 to 5,206 in 1955, an increase of 15% : new hospitals were opened at Korogwe, Lindi, Nzega, Njombe and Mbulu and the temporary tuberculosis hospital at Kibongoto was rebuilt with permanent materials. The foundation stone of a new general hospital (the Princess Margaret Hospital) at Dar es Salaam was laid in 1954 though it was not opened until 1960. In the same year (1954) the first out-patient clinic not attached to a hospital was opened at Ilala, a suburban area of Dar es Salaam; two more clinics followed in 1955 and 1958. In addition, extensive improvements and additions to existing hospitals were carried out in the early fifties. These included, among others, extensions to the Chazi leprosarium and major improvements to the Infectious Disease and Ocean Road hospitals in Dar es Salaam.

The environmental services did not increase at anything like the same rate as the personal health services. At the end of 1954, the staff of the country's environmental health services included twenty-eight health inspectors, six assistant health inspectors and sixty-three sanitary inspectors. Sleeping sickness and malaria work continued under specially detailed medical officers and the malaria unit employed two entomologists, four malaria field officers (trained by the unit for supervisory work in the provinces), twenty malaria assistants (for supervisory work at a local level), and eleven malaria auxiliaries.

In contrast the maternal and child welfare service continued to expand rapidly throughout the fifties. In 1950 there were seventy-nine government, mission and local authority maternity and child welfare clinics. By 1955, there were 188 ante-natal clinics and 119 child health clinics. Nearly 250,000 attendances were recorded at the former and over 200,000 at the latter. Expansion was particularly evident in the local authority sector; first attendances at their child health clinics rose from 3,000 in 1951 to almost 14,000 in 1956. The value of obstetric services was increasingly accepted and mothers were encouraged to attend by the free UNICEF milk which was available at the clinics.

The training of African staff proceeded along the lines laid down in the Pridie report. Facilities for training nurses and midwives were increased. In 1952, a new course with an annual intake of twelve students was established at Tukuyu to train 'health nurses'. On completion of the two-year training which included midwifery, child care, nursing, nutrition, domestic hygiene, homecraft and first-aid, the nurses were posted to rural maternity and child welfare clinics where they worked under the supervision of health visitors. Their duties were the 'teaching of hygiene and nutrition in the home, institutional work (including the conduct of maternity and child health clinics), general health teaching and school health supervision'.[17] They were not intended to act as midwives. Older women were preferred for this course as it was thought that they would exert a greater influence in the villages. In addition, 'village nurses' were trained for two years at approved mission stations. These nurses were of a lower educational standard than the health nurses, but carried out similar functions.

A limited number of 'practical' or village midwives were also trained informally at district hospitals. Generally they were women of above child-bearing age who were given a short course in the rudiments of hygiene and midwifery and who then returned to practise in their own areas.

A training school for assistant health inspectors—a new grade at a more advanced level than the existing sanitary inspectors—was opened at Kongwa in 1952. Students were required to possess Standard X education and the course was for three years. The first batch of seven students qualified in 1954 by passing the London Royal Sanitary Institute Examination. A twelve-month course for a less highly trained environmental health worker with Standard VI education was also begun at Kongwa. The first fourteen 'health orderlies' qualified in 1953 and were posted to districts for rural sanitary duties under the supervision of the district medical officer. For a time Kongwa thus became the training centre advocated by Dr. Pridie for staff to work in the field of public health—health nurses, assistant health inspectors and health orderlies.

To regulate all these different types of training, two councils were set up. The Nurses' and Midwives' Council was set up by Ordinance in 1952 and immediately revised the training syllabuses for nurses and midwives. In future nurses were to be trained for three years and midwives for two years. The Tanganyika Medical Training Board, a non-statutory body was set up in 1951 to regulate the training of all other medical auxiliary staff.

Graduates from Makerere College were licensed as assistant medical officers until legislation was enacted in 1953 which enabled students graduating under a revised medical

---

[17] *Annual Report of the Medical Department*, 1953, p. 4.

syllabus to become eligible for full registration as medical practitioners in East Africa. After completing Standard XII students were required to undergo two years of premedical education, five years of medical training and one year of internship. Some graduates of the old programme were also able to obtain registration after proof of satisfactory medical standards. By the end of 1955, however, there were still only nine East African medical graduates employed by the government, compared with sixty-one expatriate government medical officers.

Consolidation 1956-1962

In 1956, a review was made of progress since the Pridie Report and a five year development plan was laid down. This stated

> During the past five years,
> ... curative services have advanced substantially, but, in the field, development of preventive services has not been so great. The reason for this is that staff training had to be organized and a reasonable outflow of trained products had to be achieved in the first place. This has been achieved during the past five years and the Medical Department is now in a position to take concrete steps to develop preventive services in the rural areas, and by so doing to utilize effectively the trained output of departmental training establishments.[18]

The review continued by reiterating the Pridie principles on the order of priority for future development:

> ... Expansion will naturally be limited by the size of the capital sum made available to the Department, but as curative medicine is what the people understand and what they want, and as in African conditions at present preventive medicine can only hope to be accepted by the people through curative services, it is proposed to devote by far the greater part of the capital fund available from

---

[18] *A Draft Plan for the Development of Medical Services in Tanganyika—with special reference to the period 1956/61*, Dar es Salaam, 1956, p. 1.

development sources to expansion of the Hospital Services. Even this will not achieve the target of one bed per thousand in government hospitals, which was and still remains the immediate objective.

There still remained in 1956 several government hospitals without medical officers. Nevertheless, including the services provided by missions in receipt of government grants, there were very few populated areas beyond 'reasonable reach' (a radius of fifty miles) of hospital services provided or subsidized by the Government. In total there was an average of 0·6 beds (including dispensary beds) per thousand population.

The report emphasized the value of and need for health centres in the rural areas 'for providing curative and preventive health services and as a medium for health education at village level'. Although Dr. Pridie had suggested in 1949 that rural dispensaries should gradually be turned into health centres, providing both curative and preventive health care, no action had been taken. Detailed plans were now developed for such centres. They were to consist of a dispensary with a small holding ward, a maternity and child health clinic together with a delivery room and lying-in accommodation, and a health office with health education facilities. Staff housing would also be required. Eventually it was hoped that health centres would replace dispensaries, but it was recognized that lack of finance and staff would make this impossible for many years. A reasonable and practicable aim was thought to be one health centre to 40,000 or 50,000 population, supported by satellite dispensaries. It was proposed that out of a programme of 160 centres, forty should be provided in the next five years (1956-1961). Each health centre was to be staffed by one medical assistant, one health inspector, at least two village midwives, two nursing orderlies, one health orderly and two subordinate staff. All these categories of staff were already in existence. The central medical department would be responsible for training and for professional supervision of the centres. It would also employ the senior staff. The local authorities were to be responsible for constructing and maintaining the centres and for providing all equipment, including drugs and dressings. The forty health centres were expected to cost a total of £216,000 to build and equip and £53,000 a year to maintain.

The cost of the hospital development programme under the five-year plan was to be much larger. The Princess Margaret Hospital at Dar es Salaam was expected to cost £918,000 and hospital projects outside the capital were estimated at £482,000. Including the provision of housing the total capital expenditure during the five years was put at over £2 million. Current expenditure was estimated to increase from £1·6 million in 1955/56 to £2·6 million in 1960/61 though it was hoped that some part of the latter would be borne by local authorities.

Most of the additional current cost was to reflect additions to staff and to the number of students in training. In 1955/56 there was an establishment of seventy-five medical officers and sixty-eight subsidiary medical staff (assistant and senior-assistant surgeons, medical officers [East Africa], sub-assistant and senior sub-assistant surgeons), but twenty posts were unfilled. It was now considered desirable to abolish all subordinate medical grades and to have only one grade of medical officer; sub-assistant surgeons were no longer recruited. It was hoped to have by 1960/61 126 medical officers and sixty-one subordinate staff, including nineteen East African graduates, making a total of 187 medical practitioners in government service instead of the 1955/56 establishment of 143 (123 in post); the number of specialists was to be increased to twenty-one. Neither of these aims was in the event to be achieved. At the end of 1960 there were still only 143 practitioners in government service and twelve specialists.

The future of the medical assistant and rural medical aid as distinct categories had still to be settled. It was intended, the report said, that the latter should eventually be upgraded to the level of the former. However,

As there seemed little prospect of increasing substantially

the output of medical assistants and as there was a real pressure from the native authorities for larger numbers of trained men, a scheme was actually devised to produce a greater annual output of rural medical aids.

The report stated frankly that 'increased output could only be achieved at the expense of further lowering of standards'. Thus, the rural medical aid scheme was to be continued for another two or three years, until it was practicable to replace it with one medical assistant programme; this remained the long-term objective.

Other proposals were made designed to increase the annual output of newly qualified medical auxiliary personnel from a total of 183 in 1956 to 427 in 1960/61. It was also decided to introduce health education training, to place a greater emphasis on the provision of child health services, and to increase the number of trained staff from abroad, including nurses, health visitors, sister tutors, physiotherapists and health inspectors.

The 1956 plan was termed 'a feasible and realistic blueprint'.[19] It was accepted by the government as a statement of policy to be implemented 'as and when the necessary financial provision can be made available'.[20]

The necessary financial provision was not, however, made available anything like as fast as envisaged in the plan. The heyday of post-war expansion was over. Government revenue began to fall in 1956 and both in that year and in 1957 there were deficits. The health services were already drawing about 9% of the total government budget. African members were by then gaining power in the legislature. They demanded much higher expenditure on education and on economic development. In consequence, the health services were given lower priority in government spending; they should only develop in equilibrium with the economic

---

[19] *A Draft Plan for the Development of Medical Services in Tanganyika—with special reference to the period 1956/61*, Dar es Salaam, 1956, p. 50.
[20] Legislative Council of Tanganyika, *Development of Medical Services*, Dar es Salaam, 1956, p. 2.

growth of the country.[21] An *ad hoc* committee of the Legislative Council reviewed the medical plan in 1957, 're-costed in the light of salary changes and rising capital costs'. It was decided that its implementation should be spread over six or seven years instead of five. A review of the Territory's finances at the end of 1957 also led to a decision to restrict the growth of recurrent expenditure and it was in the social services that expenditure was to be 'most severely restrained'. As a result the rate of development of the medical services was to be 'somewhat slower' than in the past six or seven years.[22]

By the end of 1958 there were doubts whether the services could be maintained in the future even at their existing levels. Progress in some aspects of the plan was 'minimal', and it was clear that the relatively rapid development in the early 1950s would not be regained in the immediate future. Current expenditure on health by the Central Government only reached £1,866,407 in 1960/61 instead of the £2¼ million recommended in the five-year plan. Between 1957 and 1960 the official estimates of the population showed an increase from nearly 8·8 million to over 9·2 million. Thus, expenditure per head rose very little—from just under four shillings to just over four shillings per head.

The demand for medical attention was not, however, deterred by changes either in the economic situation or in social priorities and the numbers of patients seen by government, local authority and voluntary agency (mission) services continued to increase. The number of in-patients at government hospitals and dispensaries rose from 81,000 in 1950 to 111,000 in 1955 and 149,000 in 1960. The demand for voluntary agency services also developed rapidly in this period; the figures showed an increase from 69,000 in-patients in 1950 to 97,000 in 1955 and 143,000 in 1960. The number of out-patient first attendances at government hospitals and dispensaries rose from 1·2 million to 1·7 mil-

---

[21] *Handbook of Tanganyika*, Dar es Salaam, 1957, p. 339, and the International Bank for Reconstruction and Development, *Economic Development of Tanganyika*, Dar es Salaam, 1960.
[22] *Annual Report of the Medical Department*, 1957, p. 2.

lion between 1955 and 1960 and the demand for local authority dispensary services continued to rise at an embarrassing rate. The number of dispensaries increased from 565 in 1956 to 692 in 1960—faster than the number of trained staff : services were being expanded, it was said, beyond the resources of trained staff properly to operate such services.

Both the recruitment of staff and the operation of training programmes had to be kept within a narrow budget. During part of 1958/59 there was a 'freeze' on the recruitment of staff, and there was, moreover, difficulty in recruiting even those professional staff for whom financial provision was made. There was a net loss of two medical officers and twenty-four nursing sisters between the end of 1956 and the end of 1958 and a further loss of six nursing sisters during 1959. The 1956 plan had envisaged a net *gain* of sixty-five medical officers and eighty nursing sisters over the five years. At the end of 1959, the nursing services were reported to be in a very dangerous position. Shortage of medical assistants became so acute that a new out-patient clinic in Dar es Salaam which was completed in October, 1957 could not be opened for several months.

The policy of concentrating all government training in Dar es Salaam was, however, carried out except for the grades of health nurse and rural medical aid. The first batch of six dental assistants qualified at the end of 1957 and faced an enormous demand for their services. By 1960, there were eighteen dental assistants in government service. In 1959 the first three women medical assistants qualified and were detailed mainly for work with women patients.

In 1960, 335 students qualified from approved government and mission medical and nursing training centres. The voluntary agencies were now training almost as many students as the government centres but the majority of their students were for nursing and midwifery. In 1960, eighty-six nurses qualified from voluntary hospital schools compared with sixty-seven from the government's training centre at the Princess Margaret Hospital. All these nurses were eligible for entry to Part 'B' of the Tanganyikan register.

From the late fifties, the government and voluntary agencies sent several Tanganyika-trained nurses each year to the United Kingdom for further training to enable them to qualify for admission to Part 'A' of the Register. These students were trained for the S.R.N. and S.C.M. certificates or for mental nursing qualifications and returned to Tanganyika as nursing sisters.

In 1962 changes were made in the system of nurse training to produce a 'multipurpose' nurse who would be equipped for work either in the public health field or in the hospitals (see Chapter 9). This new grade will replace the two existing categories of hospital nurse (three-year training) and health nurse (two-year training). Candidates for the new combined three-year course will be required to have Standard VIII education and on qualification will be admitted to Part 'B' of the Tanganyikan register. The new course includes less advanced hospital instruction than was provided in the earlier three-year course, and for six months female students will study midwifery and male students have options of training in operating theatre technique, tuberculosis, leprosy or mental nursing. A selected number of promising students will be able to continue for a fourth year of hospital training to qualify for admission to Part 'A' of the Register of Nurses and the Register of Midwives. Such a nurse can then be graded as a staff nurse, with prospects of promotion to nursing sister and matron.

The long postponed plan to amalgamate the grades of medical assistant and rural medical aid was finally abandoned in 1961. By this time, the extension of secondary education had led to a reduction in the number of pupils leaving school at Standard X from which recruits for the medical assistant course had been drawn: only nineteen students started the course in 1961. It was said that

... the medical assistant is simply not good enough for the work he is required to do at a health centre. He is the officer in charge of a health service for some 50,000 people. Almost invariably he is the highest trained medical worker in the area. This area may well measure some

7,000 square miles, and often more, and he himself may well be stationed at a considerable distance from the nearest hospital. (If we ignore the unevenly distributed mission hospitals, the theoretical mean of the distance in a fully established scheme would be around fifty miles as the crow flies . . .)[23]

Clearly, the rural health centre should be headed by a doctor with additional public health qualifications; there were, however, only about 400 registered doctors working in the country and the establishment of doctors in the government service had risen from 114 to only 178 during the previous fifteen years. Confronted with the prospect of even greater medical staff shortages in the future it was decided, in 1962, to set up a new medical training course in Dar es Salaam to begin producing Tanganyika-trained practitioners—as they are referred to throughout this Report. In Chapter 9 we outline the content and aims of this new medical course. The Government, in reaching this decision, decided at the same time that there should be no more courses leading to the grade of medical assistant; a number of selected medical assistants began another new course enabling them to be upgraded to the assistant medical officer level. Upgrading of dental assistants to assistant dental officers and of assistant health inspectors to health inspectors was also initiated.

Rural medical aids continue to be trained. A new rural health centre at Ifakara was opened in July, 1961, under Professor Geigy of Basle University, which was first used to give a special three-month course as part of the rural medical aid curriculum. A further school for training rural medical aids has been established at Bukoba, this time with Scandinavian aid.

Rural health centres have developed slowly. Of the forty envisaged in the five-year plan, ten were opened in 1958; all but one were extensions of existing dispensaries. There were only nineteen in operation by 1960 and twenty-two by

[23] Medical Education with Particular Reference to the needs of Tanganyika: Paper submitted by Chief Medical Officer Tanganyika to Medical Faculty Board of Makerere College, 1962.

the end of 1961. Local authorities are reported to have 'accepted with alacrity' the need for health centres in their areas, but they were not able to back their enthusiasm with the necessary finance. Moreover, the cost of constructing a health centre had risen from £5,000 (estimated in 1956) to between £6,000 and £10,000. The recurrent cost had risen to between £1,500 and £2,000 a year.

Apart from the continuously expanding maternity and child welfare services, little progress has been made since 1956 in developing the public health services. The nuclei of two central government special units have, however, been established—one for nutrition and one for health education. The former consists of one medical officer detailed for this important educational work. The latter initially included a senior medical officer, a health visitor and a health inspector supported by a central library of pictures, posters, film strips and slides.

This short historical survey shows that the progress of the services has again and again been limited by the hard realities of finance. The level of world commodity prices has been one of the more powerful forces in determining the fluctuations in the health budget and, consequently, the rate at which staff could be recruited and trained to man the dispensaries, health centres, clinics, public health agencies and hospitals. In each successive wave of economy it has been the preventive services which have suffered most. The decision of the government to give priority to the hospitals and curative work generally—'it is what the people want'—and the less dramatic appeal of prevention and public health were also contributing factors.

Yet there has been no lack of careful thought about the present and the future; no shortage of plans—indeed, three major programmes were formulated within ten post-war years—and ample evidence of enthusiasm for a better health service. But none of these programmes has proved to be within the economic capacity of the country. Progress, where it has been achieved, has quickly been caught up by population growth and rising demands.

The lessons of this history are clear. If a health plan for

31

Tanganyika is to progress beyond the stage of ideas and ideals it must be firmly based on the realities of economics and population. It is for this reason that we make these our starting points in Chapter 4.

2 The Health Services and their Problems Today

The Minister for Health is responsible to the Government of Tanganyika for providing, directly or indirectly, a balanced curative and preventive health service for the whole country. Historically, as we have shown in the previous chapter, central government has never provided all the services. From the earliest years, missionary societies (or voluntary agencies as we will call them for the remainder of this report) established mainly rural hospital and dispensary services. More recently, local authorities have developed a network of rural dispensaries, staffed by rural medical aids and dressers. Medical services have also been developed by certain large employers of labour—chiefly the mines and plantations.

The four sectors of 'organized' health services maintain a total of 18,832 beds throughout Tanganyika, in hospitals and in bedded dispensaries. A large proportion of these beds are attached to dispensaries or are in very small hospitals which have extremely limited facilities. Some of them are no more than 'resting beds' in holding units where patients stay overnight awaiting treatment or transfer. Including all these beds, there are two beds per thousand of the population; but at least a third of the beds are not regularly supervised by a doctor, and less than half have a doctor resident on the premises. Even in some hospitals with a resident doctor the facilities are very rudimentary.

In Table I we set out the total of hospital and dispensary beds by their ownership.

Table I

Hospital and Dispensary Beds in Tanganyika at 31st December, 1961

	Number of Hospitals or Dispensaries	Number of Beds
Central Government		
General Hospitals . .	47	5,197
Special Hospitals . .	5	1,365
Dispensaries . . .	21	466
Total:		7,028
Local Government		
Rural Health Centres and Dispensaries . . .	737	1,795
Voluntary Agencies		
Hospitals with doctors .	48	4,724
Dispensaries (over 20 beds) .	64	2,905
Dispensaries (less than 20 beds)	175	721
Total:		8,350
Occupational Services		
Hospitals and Dispensaries .	246	1,659
Total Treatment Units:	1,343*	18,832

*This total includes Local Government and Occupational dispensaries without beds.

This total of 18,832 beds does not include the care of leprosy patients other than those classified as receiving 'hospital' care either because of illness other than leprosy, because of reaction to drugs, or because of therapeutic surgery. Accommodation for leprosy patients not regarded as requiring 'hospital' care is provided by central government, voluntary agencies and local authorities. Special grants are paid by the central government to the voluntary agencies for the supply of drugs and for the maintenance of infectious cases. These grants are not included in the main grant scheme to agencies described later in this chapter. In total there were 4,464 leprosy patients resident in leprosaria on 30th November 1961; also resident were 913 persons who were not suffering from leprosy. Most of the nineteen leprosaria and 411 out-patient clinics for leprosy were provided by voluntary agencies. Over 30,000 cases were treated in 1961, the majority of them old cases; just over 8,000 were new cases.

In the last five years the number of out-patients at government hospitals has increased by more than one-third and the number at local authority dispensaries has almost doubled. At Mnazi Mmoja Clinic in Dar es Salaam, we saw patients overflowing the physical capacity of the building, standing or sitting anywhere they could find space. In these conditions the medical care attempted could only be scanty. Adequate physical examinations cannot be carried out in circumstances of such pressure. What is praiseworthy is that the quality of medical care provided in such conditions is as good as it is. The population of Tanganyika owes much to the dedicated service of its medical auxiliaries. Yet the increase in quantity of services rendered may be disguising or contributing to a decline in quality. The impressive utilization figures which follow in Table II must, therefore, be interpreted with caution. In the absence of any information on the quality of care, it is impossible to generalize about the actual value of the treatments attempted. It cannot be high in areas where undertrained and unsupervised auxiliaries have been seeing up to three hundred patients a day.

Patients admitted to hospitals which have a resident medical practitioner are almost invariably examined by

35

'him'. Out-patients are more usually seen by a medical assistant at a central government out-patient clinic and either by a doctor or a nurse at a voluntary agency *hospital* clinic. In the local authority services the vast bulk of patients are seen either by a rural medical aid or a dresser. Thus, in view of the general lack of domiciliary services, one might guess that only about one patient in ten is seen by a medical practitioner. Consultation with a medical assistant is probably not much more frequent. Something like three-quarters of the attendances are with rural medical aids or tribal dressers. These are the *real* medical practitioners of Tanganyika at the present time.

Table II

Utilization of Medical Services, 1961

	Number of In-patient Admissions	Number of Out-patient Cases (first attendances)
Central Government	160,941	1,996,882
Local Authority	—	6,506,263
Voluntary Agency	152,298	1,239,510
Occupational	39,085	679,689
Total:	352,324	10,422,344

Though certain voluntary agencies have recently begun to play some modest part in immunization and health education campaigns, public health services are almost entirely the responsibility of central and local government. The only notable exceptions are the maternity and child welfare services where the voluntary agencies make a large contribution. Table III sets out the figures for these services in 1961.

Table III

Maternity and Child Welfare Services, 1961

	Number of Clinics	First Attendances
Ante-Natal Services		
Central Government .	71	48,667
Local Authority . .	204	68,601
Voluntary Agency .	137	59,946
Total:	412	177,214
Child Health Services		
Central Government .	69	29,715
Local Authority . .	195	52,635
Voluntary Agency .	190	54,154
Total:	454	136,504

A rapidly growing demand for maternity and child welfare clinics is reflected in the statistics over the last ten years. The number of confinements attended by trained staff, for example, rose from a total of about 23,000 in 1951 to over 67,000 in 1961. No estimate is available for the total number of births in Tanganyika. The Bureau of Statistics assumes a crude birth rate of 45 per 1,000.[1] This would suggest that over 400,000 children are born each year; in other words, one delivery in every six was attended by trained staff in 1961.

Central Government Health Services

The government health services are organized on the three-tiered administrative pattern found in other Tanganyikan

[1] *Population Studies* (Cambridge University Press, 1953) **7**, No. 2.

government departments: the Ministry, the Region (formerly Province) and the District. At the top, the health division of the Ministry of Health and Labour[2] is headed by the Chief Medical Officer who has to assist him in Dar es Salaam a deputy, three principal medical officers, the principal matron and the chief health inspector. Certain special services are supervised directly by medical head-quarters—medical training, the pathology and pharmaceutical services, the psychiatric service and certain specialist units (malaria, health education and nutrition). All other services, comprising the bulk of the personal and environmental services provided directly by central government, are delegated to nine regional medical officers and to the medical superintendent of the Dar es Salaam hospitals which virtually comprise a tenth region.

Regional medical officers, all of whom are of senior medical officer rank, are responsible to the Chief Medical Officer for the day to day organization of both the personal and environmental health services within their respective regions. According to the particular interests of the individual officer and depending on the volume of work in the region, some of them have taken on executive responsibilities for part of their time. Thus, the regional medical officers for the Northern and Eastern regions act as medical officers of health for the towns in which their regional headquarters are situated—Arusha and Morogoro respectively. Several regional officers undertake clinical or other work in a regional or district hospital. The regional officer in the Western region acts also as the territorial sleeping sickness officer, and the Tanga regional officer acts as the regional tuberculosis officer. In addition, a regional officer may have to discharge other duties when a district medical officer falls sick or is on leave.

The average region is divided into five or six districts, each of which is supervised by a district medical officer responsible to the regional medical officer. The administrative headquarters of a district are usually at a hospital which the district medical officer supervises. He is also expected to

---

[2] Now two separate Ministries.

38

supervise local authority health centres (where they exist) and dispensaries in the district. Some of these districts are of considerable size. The largest, Tabora district, covers an area of some 25,000 square miles and has a population of over 166,000.[3] It is not surprising that the district medical officer, who is often in clinical charge of the only hospital in the area, fails to perform effectively his supervisory functions. Bad communications, accentuated during the rainy season, mean much unproductive time spent in travelling in these extensive districts, parts of which may be quite inaccessible by road for several months of the year.

Central government maintains forty-seven general hospitals of which two are in Dar es Salaam. The nine hospitals situated at the regional administrative headquarters are termed regional hospitals, although most of them are not substantially different from district hospitals. Table IV shows the size of these forty-seven hospitals.

Table IV

Distribution of Government General Hospitals by Size at 31st December, 1961

Number of Beds	Number of Hospitals
0– 49	10
50– 99	20
100–199	11
200–299	4
300–399	—
400–499	1
500 and above	1
	—
	47
	—

[3] See *Statistical Abstract, 1961*, Dar es Salaam, 1961, p. 22.

The Health Services of Tanganyika

There is only one government general hospital in Tanganyika with more than 500 beds: the Princess Margaret Hospital in Dar es Salaam with 762 beds at the end of 1961. The only other sizeable unit is Tanga Hospital with 410 beds. All the other forty-five regional and district hospitals have less than 300 beds: thirty of them have less than 100 beds. Because of their position in the administrative centre of a large geographical area, regional hospitals tend to be large but there are no clear-cut distinctions. In the relatively prosperous Northern region there are four government general hospitals, of which three have over 100 beds.

Patients are referred or find their way to government hospitals either directly from the town in which the hospital is situated or from rural dispensaries, most of which are run by local authorities. The few dispensaries run by the central government are mainly in areas which are not yet served by local authority services. For some years it has been the policy of the government not to set up dispensaries where local authority services already exist, and to hand over dispensaries to local authorities as soon as they are able to manage them. There are at present (31st December, 1961) twenty-one bedded dispensaries maintained by central government. They are run as satellites of a district hospital and are generally supervised by medical assistants. The smallest of these has ten and the largest forty-four beds; some of these beds may be set aside for maternity cases (six dispensaries), tuberculosis (two dispensaries) and infectious diseases (five dispensaries).

In theory, a patient from a rural area can be referred through his local authority dispensary to a district hospital and then via the regional hospital to the full range of specialist services which are only available at Dar es Salaam. In practice this rarely happens. Apart from other difficulties, transport facilities are far from adequate—particularly in the rainy season. There are ambulance services attached to the hospitals within the main towns and local authorities maintain vehicles if they can afford the cost. One administrator guessed that half of the patients at Dodoma Hospital came from over ten miles away.

The Health Services and their Problems Today

When a patient is being transported from an outlying central government dispensary to a hospital, or from one hospital to another, the government will arrange and pay for transport. In other cases assistance towards bus and train fares may be provided by local authorities. But in most cases the patient faced with these difficulties (unless obviously in an emergency condition) will never proceed beyond the skill of the only 'practitioner' available to him locally—a dresser or a rural medical aid.

The Princess Margaret Hospital in Dar es Salaam, opened in 1960, offers accommodation and facilities of a standard not far below that of the best non-teaching hospital in the United Kingdom. At the end of 1961, out of the total of 762 beds, 464 were for general patients. The main hospital is supplemented by the Ocean Road Hospital which adds 75 obstetric beds to the capital's hospital bed complement, making a total of about 840 beds in Dar es Salaam. Dar es Salaam, which has little over one per cent of the population of the country, contains one-sixth of all government general hospital beds. *One-fifth* of the government's medical care budget is spent in the city. The specialist services are also heavily concentrated in Dar es Salaam : and more than a quarter of the total expenditure on medical staff salaries attributable to the hospital and dispensary services is paid to staff attached to the Dar es Salaam hospitals. This concentration of facilities in Dar es Salaam is explicable, of course, on the grounds that it is intended that it should be the national reference and specialist centre as well as a training centre. A recent check revealed that 27% of all patients admitted to the Dar es Salaam hospitals gave addresses outside the city. A further unknown proportion also came from outside the city but gave the Dar es Salaam address of a relative with whom they were staying.

By contrast, however, there is not yet a government general hospital in each of the fifty-six districts. In the Masasi district of the Southern region, a voluntary agency hospital is functioning and is reimbursed as a district hospital. Even here, however, the hospital doctor has not taken over all the functions of a district medical officer : the local authority dispensaries in the hospital's catchment area are supervised by a government doctor from the adjoining district. The grant-aided voluntary hospitals in each region are theoretically supervised by the regional medical officer but are seldom linked with the government hospital and dispensary system.

Though most of the central government hospitals are 'general', many set aside a number of beds for maternity cases and for cases of infectious disease. About one-third of the regional and district hospitals make special provision for tuberculosis patients. There are no facilities for treating the mentally ill in the regional and district hospitals system other than eleven 'holding beds' in Dar es Salaam. This recently built unit consists of a number of barred cells and is not suitable for modern psychiatric treatment. There is a plan to establish psychiatric units in Dar es Salaam and in the regional general hospitals, but the continuing shortage of funds has so far prevented these plans from being implemented. The mental hospital services are mainly under the control of the central government. There are in addition, a 140-bed hospital run by the Lutheran Mission at Lutindi for long-stay cases and a new hospital at Lushoto opened in mid-1962 which in its first stage is being built to accommodate up to 200 patients, both long-stay and convalescent. The government maintains two related mental hospitals at Dodoma, in the Central region, with a combined total of 992 beds: Mirembe Hospital, with 746 beds, accommodates both acute and long-stay cases, while Isanga Hospital, with 246 beds, accommodates patients who are referred for psychiatric treatment through the courts on criminal charges. Both hospitals come directly under the control of the medical department and are administered by the same staff.

As the only acute mental hospital in Tanganyika, Mirembe Hospital cannot refuse admission to referred patients, some of whom have had to make difficult journeys of hundreds of miles and may be exhausted and debilitated on arrival. The hospital is invariably overcrowded. At 31st December 1961 there were 787 patients in Mirembe Hospital —forty-one above the official bed complement. Extra accommodation is available but there is at present no money with which to staff it. The combined hospitals have two psychiatrists (until recently only one), the senior of whom acts as medical superintendent of the hospitals and as government psychiatrist. In the latter capacity he visits Dar es Salaam once a month to hold a psychiatric out-patient clinic; he is also required to attend sessions of the High Court in various parts of the country for cases (usually of murder) where the question of sanity is involved. These duties and the administrative work of the hospital (Mirembe has no lay administrator) take up one-third of his time. There are no qualified African mental nurses; this situation will be remedied at the end of 1963 when the first batch of students returns from training in the United Kingdom.

All hospitals in Tanganyika suffer in varying degrees from lack of funds, but the financial position of Mirembe Hospital is particularly strained. The patients are housed, fed, clothed and treated for an average cost of only four shillings a day, of which one shilling goes on food. These figures are in line with other government long-stay hospitals but not with those giving acute, short-stay treatment. About half the patients at Mirembe stay for less than one year and the length of stay ranges upwards from a few weeks.

Patients are sent to Mirembe from all over the country. In 1961, 477 patients were admitted under certificate, ninety-three for observation and forty-six on a voluntary basis. Frequently the patient is first taken to the police by friends or relatives and is locked in the local prison. After medical examination, the doctor's report is then sent to a magistrate and if the patient is certified, he is sent to Dodoma by train, accompanied by warders.

On arrival many patients are found to be suffering also from one or more major physical illnesses—malaria, pneumonia, hookworm infestation or bilharzia. This combination of physical and mental disease creates further problems for the mental hospital staff. A considerable part of the drug budget, for example, is spent on vitamins and antibiotics. Treatment for most patients consist mainly of electro-convulsive therapy and drugs. The hospital has no contact, direct or indirect, with discharged patients and there are no mental welfare services of any kind in Tanganyika. There are plans for seconding mental welfare staff from Mirembe to the regions but these, like the proposed regional psychiatric units, have been postponed because of lack of finance.

The central government is responsible for three other 'special hospitals'. Kibongoto Hospital for tuberculosis patients, on the slopes of Kilimanjaro, has 302 beds for in-patients and supervises a number of out-patient and follow-up services. The two small leprosy hospitals in Eastern and Southern Highlands regions maintain a total of seventy-one beds. Unlike the mental hospitals, which are directly responsible to the Ministry, these hospitals are administered through the regional hospital system.

Central government is thus responsible for some 5,200 beds in general hospitals, some 1,000 beds in mental hospitals, over 350 beds in special hospitals and over 450 beds in satellite dispensaries: in all about 7,000 beds. The distribution of these beds is summarized in Table V. Out of every 100 beds provided by central government, sixty are designated for general short-stay patients, fourteen for the mentally ill, fourteen for tuberculosis cases, seven for obstetrics, and five for infectious diseases. This division does not reflect the morbidity of the patients who are admitted to hospital. Infectious and parasitic diseases are the most frequent cause of in-patient admissions to hospitals in Tanganyika, followed by obstetrical cases and diseases of the respiratory system; nearly a third of all deaths in hospitals in 1960 were attributed to infectious or parasitic diseases.

The central government and most local authorities offer free services. In the case of central government the free patients are called Grade IV patients. For Grades III, II, and I, increasing scales of charges are levied for greater comfort and convenience and in some respects for better medical treatment. The facilities provided in these higher grades are, however, available free to substantive government officers and their families as a basic condition of service—provided the injury or illness is not due to indiscretion or negligence on the part of the officer. Accouchement fees, however, are

Table V

Accommodation in Central Government Hospitals and Dispensaries at 31st December, 1961

	Number of Hospitals	No. of Wards	No. and Category of Beds					Total beds
			General	Obstetrics	Tuberculosis	Infectious	Mental	
General Hospitals								
Dar es Salaam .	2	62	518	65	188	55	11	837
Regional and District Hospitals . .	45	394	3,309	369	474	208	—	4,360
Mental Hospitals .	2	55	—	—	—	—	992	992
Special Hospitals								
Tuberculosis .	1	7	—	—	302	—	—	302
Leprosy . .	2	7	1	3	—	67	—	71
Dispensaries . .	21	66	388	27	26	25	—	466
Total:	73	591	4,216	464	990	355	1,003	7,028

charged. The grade to which officials and their dependants are referred depends on the salary of the officer. The charge for an in-patient in Grade I is fifty shillings to sixty shillings a day (according to the hospital : Princess Margaret Hospital, for example, commands the higher rate.) A Grade II in-patient pays thirty shillings to thirty-five shillings a day. These charges include all board and nursing fees : additional fees are payable in respect of specific medical procedures. Grade III in-patients pay a flat rate of six shillings for every three days or part of three days. This charge is payable in advance.

Grades of out-patients' clinics are distinguished by the grade of officer in charge of them. Normally Grade I patients are seen by a medical officer, Grades III and IV patients by a medical assistant; Grade II has recently been abolished as a grade for out-patients. Grade I patients are only given twenty-four hours' supply of drugs and have to pay for later supplies. Out-patient fees are twenty shillings per visit for Grade I patients (ten shillings for children under fourteen years) and two shillings per visit for Grade III patients. Grade IV patients are seen without charge. Since the out-patient departments of hospitals are usually thronged with Grade IV patients, the Grade III charge acts to some extent as an 'amenity' charge. Clinics for the different grades are held at different times of the day and week. Thus the patient with a little money is able to pay for the privilege of a less crowded out-patient list, generally attention earlier in the day, and the possibility of more time being allotted to him by the medical assistant.

Since 1st July 1962, doctors employed by central government have been disallowed private practice. They do, however, receive in addition to their salary one-third of the fees paid to the government by Grades I and II patients for specific procedures undertaken by them. An obstetrician, for example, would receive one-third of the accouchement fees paid by patients in these grades, according to the government fee schedule. The total sum thus paid out in 1961/62 was £19,000—obstetrics being the largest source of such payments. The sum for any particular doctor varies both according to his type of practice (the charges for some procedures are greater than for others) and to the number of Grades I and II patients he sees (no extra sums are payable according to the number of Grades III and IV patients who are seen).

The Adu Report[4] recommended the abolition of both types of private practice, both the extra-governmental and the intra-governmental just described. Rates of compensation of £200 or £400 per year were suggested. These recommendations have not been implemented. Instead, private practice by government doctors has been restricted to the acceptance of intra-mural fees laid down by regulation. The abolition of extra-mural private practice by government doctors has made it easier for private practitioners to set up in practice in some of the towns: one government doctor has resigned to do just this.

In March 1962 the government employed ten specialists, four pathologists and 145 other medical practitioners. The government also employed thirty-two assistant medical officers and 198 medical assistants. We do not have the figures for the deployment of medical assistants at that date, but it is probably not dissimilar to that for September 1961 when there were 186 medical assistants employed by the central government. Of these, twenty-four were seconded to local authorities to run rural health centres, twenty were allocated to run the government dispensaries and fourteen others were employed solely on out-patient work in Dar es Salaam. The remaining government medical assistants were working in government hospitals, either acting as house officers or caring for Grades III and IV out-patients.

So far we have described the curative services in some detail as a background to the recommendations we make in later chapters. It is clear from our analysis of the budget figures that they now play a dominating role. Some of the reasons for this trend in health priorities were outlined in Chapter 1. One has been the popular demand for—and the more dramatic appeal of—hospital treatment. Secondly, it has been believed for some years that preventive measures

---

[4] *Report of the Tanganyika Salaries Commission*, Dar es Salaam, 1961.

could not be successfully developed on a broad front unless they were based on a soundly established system of curative medicine—a complete reversal of the roles played by preventive and curative measures in Britain in the nineteenth century. Thirdly—and as a statement of historical fact—whenever the country has had to face the need for financial retrenchment it has been the preventive services which have suffered first and suffered most.

To fulfil our terms of reference we had to consider this question of priorities between prevention and cure—despite all the difficulties of distinguishing them and defining them in practice. While it is not possible, therefore, to measure in any precise way the role of the preventive services in the health budget we present in Table VI as detailed a functional breakdown of the central government budget as we have been able to develop.[5]

In the financial year 1961/62, the health division of the Ministry of Health and Labour was responsible for a gross expenditure of almost £2·4 million. Of this sum, about £172,000 should be subtracted—the bulk of it being expenditure on stores purchased for re-sale to outside bodies. In Table VI we show the breakdown of the remaining £2·2 million.

Medical headquarters accounts for £126,000, a little under 6% of the total budget. This includes administration of the central medical stores, which supply drugs and equipment to all government units and to the grant-aided voluntary agencies and local authorities. The medical and dental care categories account for 80% of the total government health budget. More than one-fifth of this sum (£383,000) is spent on the Dar es Salaam hospitals. Approximately £21,000 was spent on dental care; the establishment of dental personnel in March 1962 included seven dental surgeons (only four in post), six assistant dental officers, three dental technicians and fourteen dental assistants, with the responsibility of providing a dental service for the whole of Tanganyika. The pathology service is shown separately because it is centrally administered; the

---

[5] See also Appendix B for a more detailed analysis.

48

Table VI

*Ministry of Health and Labour: Functional Breakdown
of Health Expenditure (gross figures) 1961/62*

	£'000s	Percentages
Headquarters . . .	126	6
Medical and Dental Care:		
Dar es Salaam . . .	383	17
Regional general services .	1,151	52
Mental Hospitals . .	79	4
Other special hospitals .	47	2
Dental care . . .	21	1
Pathology service . .	58	3
Other	19	1
Public Health . . .	111	5
Teaching and Research .	37	2
Grants and fees for service to voluntary agencies, private practitioners etc. . .	172	8
Total:	2,204	100%

central pathology laboratory at Dar es Salaam supervises the regional laboratories.

Although we have included a subdivision for 'Teaching and Research' no Ministry of Health money is specifically put aside for research.[6] Some research is, however, undertaken by Ministry of Health staff in the course of other duties, notably by the epidemiology (formerly malaria) unit. Thus, the sum of £37,000 under this head consists wholly of expenditure on the government's training programmes al-

---

[6] Medical research is a responsibility of the East African Common Services Organization. In 1960/61 Tanganyika contributed £35,198 out of the total contribution of East African governments of £104,246 for medical research in the East African countries. This sum is not part of the vote of the Ministry of Health.

most all of which are now concentrated at the Princess Margaret Training Centre in Dar es Salaam.

The government also sponsors student training for medicine and related subjects abroad. There is no university medical school in Tanganyika. However, 108 students from Tanganyika, sponsored by various organizations including the government, are at present overseas undertaking undergraduate or postgraduate studies in medicine and surgery, in addition to thirty-one who are at the Medical School of the University of East Africa at Mulago, Uganda (Makerere University College). A further 108 are taking nursing courses, thirty-one are studying pharmacy, and twenty others are taking other ancillary medical subjects. Only a minority of these students are African.[7]

The item of £172,000 for 'grants and fees' consisted of cash grants-in-aid to approved voluntary hospitals of £152,000, a further £8,000 worth of drugs and equipment supplied in kind to the voluntary hospitals, and £12,000 paid out to reimburse private medical institutions and private practitioners for services provided by them on behalf of the government.

Only 5% of the total central government budget— £111,000—was devoted to those public health services which could be separately distinguished in the accounts. Two local authorities, Dar es Salaam and Tanga, employ full-time medical officers of health. In these two cases the towns control and pay for the services. A number of townships have active sanitary authorities, but urban sanitary conditions are still far from satisfactory and in some cases are deplorable.[8] In all other cases, covering almost the entire population, the responsibility for providing public health services rests firmly with central government, through its regional medical officers. The City Council of Dar es Salaam in 1961 spent an estimated £95,000 on public health services, out of a total city budget of £763,000. Its services

[7] See Chapter 9 for more details on recruitment and training. The figures are taken from the *List of Post Secondary Students studying outside the country and at the University College 1961/62*, Dar es Salaam.
[8] *Township Sanitation Report*, Dar es Salaam, 1957.

included mosquito, rodent and pest control, a school health service (the only such service in Tanganyika), tuberculosis control and child welfare, a vaccination centre and the usual range of health inspectorate duties. The Dar es Salaam public health budget was almost as large as the public health expenditure of the government for almost the whole of the rest of the country.

In the early twenties, environmental health services were wholly separated from the personal health services. There were in fact two separate branches of health services—the medical branch and the sanitation branch. Thus, doctors in government service were seconded for duty as either medical officers or sanitation officers. Gradually these two branches have been brought together in the organization of the Ministry's work. Today, except in the two autonomous municipalities, the same medical officers are responsible for both fields of work.

Trends in the health inspectorate service have lagged behind developments in the curative services. The number of fully qualified health inspectors in post in March, 1962, was only twenty-nine, of whom twelve were African—fifteen short of the approved establishment. This serious deficiency has contributed to the relative neglect of environmental conditions. The establishment also included ninety assistant and senior assistant health inspectors, thirty-four sanitary inspectors and ninety-nine health orderlies. In 1929, 218 trained district sanitary inspectors were deployed by the government throughout Tanganyika.

At the regional level, responsibility for the environmental services falls upon the regional medical officer who has one or two health inspectors on his staff whose task it is to supervise the environmental health of the whole region. It is envisaged that eventually a fully qualified health inspector will be posted in each district but the present shortage of trained staff prevents this development. Meanwhile, the supervision of environmental health at the district level is the responsibility of the assistant health inspector.

The assistant health inspector is generally based on an office in a township or large settlement. His duties include food and milk control and general sanitation, but not malaria control. Under his supervision a group of subordinate staff, the town sanitation squad, perform such manual work as drainage and refuse removal.

Environmental health services are almost non-existent in the rural areas. The rural health centre was intended to act as a focus for both curative and preventive medicine in the country areas, but there are at present too few of these to have much effect. An assistant health inspector is attached to each of the twenty-two rural health centres which do exist. His work consists chiefly of health information and education. Health visitors and health nurses may also work from rural health centres, but they are primarily based upon separate maternity and child welfare clinics. The present government establishment includes a total provision for twenty-three health visitors and eighty-two health nurses. The health nurse as a separate staff grade has now been abolished and no more training courses are being given. They will eventually be superseded by graduates from the three-year 'general purpose' nursing course which will combine training for both hospital and public health work.

In addition to the regional organization, the government provides special units which are administered centrally to deal with particular aspects of public health work. These include an epidemiology unit and units concerned with sleeping sickness, health education, nutrition and port health. The most important in terms of size is the epidemiology unit—the former malaria unit under a new name—based in Morogoro. The professional staff consists of a malariologist and two entomologists. In addition, the unit employs five malaria field officers, two of whom are stationed at Morogoro. The other three are stationed at three of the regional headquarters where they work with the regional health inspector. The malaria field officer is of school certificate education. He is given an in-service training by the malariologist, but has no other qualification. Under him in the regions for which he is responsible are malaria assistants, who are administrators on the level of assistant health inspectors. The malaria assistant is responsible for supervising a mosquito control squad in a settlement of 3,000 people or more. This squad includes both drainers and oilers. In a small settlement there might be three drainers and three oilers under the charge of the malaria assistant.

The malaria assistant (at present forty are employed) has also been trained through an in-service course at the unit. This post is now, however, obsolescent. In the future his functions are to be taken over by an assistant health inspector who will co-ordinate all environmental health services at the settlement level. Assistant health inspectors will be given special training to enable them to undertake these further duties.

The work of the epidemiology unit consists primarily in the organization and supervision of mosquito control in townships. The research undertaken by members of the unit also includes the study of the effectiveness of control methods —particularly the use of new antimalarial drugs.

Vaccination campaigns are carried out by the health inspectorate. The only vaccine which is widely used is that for smallpox. It is known that nearly two million doses were issued in 1960. In the case of typhoid and paratyphoid, 15,600 cc. were issued. Though there has never been a substantiated case of yellow-fever in Tanganyika, to comply with international regulations there were 18,300 issues of yellow-fever vaccine. There were 6,000 issues of polio vaccine, and 500 issues of rabies vaccine. The issues of other vaccines were negligible. Triple vaccine (diphtheria, whooping cough and tetanus) is, however, now available free through UNICEF. The possibilities of taking advantage of this offer to any great extent are considerably limited by the need for refrigerated storage, and the shortage of staff to administer injections. The control of sleeping sickness, from which thirty-one people died in hospital in 1960, is the part-time responsibility of a regional medical officer who has a special interest in this disease. Serious epidemic outbreaks of diseases such as plague or poliomyelitis are dealt with by an *ad hoc* team drawn from the ranks of serving officers.

Although related studies and schemes may emerge from the work of the present epidemiology unit or from special schemes such as the Pare-Taveta residual spray scheme against malaria, no comprehensive social and epidemiological research has been allowed for. A WHO grant has been given to Makerere College in Uganda to find out what studies should be made to facilitate the mounting of preventive medical campaigns in East Africa. So far no work under this heading has been undertaken in Tanganyika. The government's health education unit consists almost entirely of the work of one doctor, as does the unit set up specifically for nutrition.

Ministry of Health expenditure attributable directly to public health as distinct from personal health service is set out in the following Table.

Table VII

Ministry of Health Expenditure on Different Public Health Services (1961/62)

	£'000
Malaria control unit	20
Trypanosomiasis control	1
Health education	5
Nutrition	2
Port health	4
Health inspectorate and other health staff .	79
Total:	111

These estimates exclude the time spent by practising clinical medical officers and other staff on health education or other public health programmes such as tuberculosis control. They do not bring into account *all* the expenditure on central government maternity and child welfare services : only the salaries of the trained staff concerned are included in the figures. Nor have we any estimates for health and environmental programmes carried out by the community development and other government departments.

Despite these gaps the value of £111,000 for 1961/62 may —for purposes of comparison—be set against the sum of £22,600 spent by the sanitation branch of the health department in 1921/22. Allowing for price changes, the amount which could be purchased with this sum was very similar. But in 1921/22 the amount spent was more than one quarter of the whole government budget for health; in 1961/62 the proportion was about 5%.

In the last year or so, the impetus for improved environmental health services and health education in a broad sense in the rural areas has been developed not so much by the Ministry of Health and Labour as through government-encouraged community self-help schemes. Not only are mass literacy campaigns and the formation of women's clubs (there were more than 400 such clubs at the end of 1960) having an important effect in raising general standards of education and living, which have a direct bearing on the community level of health; in many cases public health activities *per se* are being undertaken in this way. A few examples must suffice. In the Ihanja Chiefdom at Singida, five women social development assistants started in 1960 an experiment in mass education among women. Their aims were 'to raise minimum standards of health, child care and nutrition among 3,000 women in two years'. In another chiefdom in the same district a combined operations team consisting of an agricultural assistant, an assistant health inspector and a veterinary assistant, led by a social development assistant, persuaded—among other achievements— eighty families to put windows in their huts. In many areas water schemes—the construction of wells and the capping of springs—are being undertaken and a general awareness of community needs is being encouraged through the establishment of village development committees.

Special courses on home economics for village leaders; the establishment of residential training centres, the pioneering of new methods of teaching at village level about the elements of nutrition, child care, vegetable production, and the germ theory of infection, and other means of guiding community self-help were making, by 1962, a major contribution to the improvement of social conditions. TANU, through its representatives at every level, is encouraging all these standard-raising developments. The people of Tanganyika are now not only demanding, but actively creating, economic and social change. An important share of this effort has been devoted to problems of rural health and hygiene.

Apart from the services which the health division of the Ministry of Health and Labour itself organizes and provides, the Ministry has responsibilities for services provided by other agencies. These it exercises through professional supervision, licensing and grant-aid.

We discuss the question of registration and licensing in Chapter 9. Apart from registration, the health division does not supervise the work of private medical practitioners. But the Ministry, through its regional medical officers, does supervise to a varying extent all the organized services, the voluntary agency services and the local authority services. It should be clearly stated, however, that regional medical officers are not in a position to exercise executive control over these health services.

Closer connections between central government and other services have been encouraged in recent years by two separate developments. The first is the rural health centre. This is, in a sense, a joint central and local government venture but, as explained later, few have been constructed and the few that do exist are not all operating in the most effective way. The second, and older, development which has played a part in bringing about some measure of co-ordination in the medical services is the increasing amount of money being paid each year to approved voluntary agencies in the form of direct subsidies or grants-in-aid. The amount of money paid out in this way represents about 7% of the total government health budget and between 20 and 40% of the expenditure of the voluntary agencies on medical services. To some extent, as described later, the grant system is being used by the government as an instrument of planning policy. There is, however, no formal system of 'follow-up' in the form of co-ordinating committees at the district or regional level to link the services in each area. The only formal machinery for co-ordination is the Mission Medical Advisory Committee which is described later.

Local Authority Health Services

The evolution of the local authority health services was described in Chapter 1 and some reference has already been made to them in this chapter. In the towns, the local authorities at present provide the usual urban sanitation, inspectorate and other public health services but, as mentioned earlier, only two towns (Dar es Salaam and Tanga) employ full-time medical officers of health. Some other towns use the part-time services of government officers. Morogoro, for example, has the part-time services of the regional medical officer.

In the rural areas, local authorities provide the 'curative' services through their out-patient dispensaries, but public health services are paid for by the central government. It is the long-term policy of the Ministry that government health inspectors will eventually be transferred to local government.

The rural health services, although they have expanded rapidly year by year, still largely reflect their historical origins: they provide first-aid and first-line diagnostic services through a network of dispensaries, health centres, and maternity and child welfare clinics which are usually but not always attached to dispensaries and health centres.

The rural services are thus primarily first-aid and clinical services: there were, at the end of 1961, 737 dispensaries and health centres, 204 ante-natal clinics and 195 child health clinics. Two out of every five new maternity and child welfare patients and more than three out of every five other new patients are seen in these local authority units.

Under the five-year plan of 1956 it was intended that forty out of the target of 160 health centres would be constructed by 1961. But by the end of that year only twenty-two were in existence. The principal staff of a health centre consists of a medical assistant, an assistant health inspector and a health

57

nurse. Local authorities are responsible for capital construction and all running costs. The medical assistant and health nurse, although paid for by the local authorities, are in fact seconded by and remain employees of central government. This enables the central government to supervise their work and to threaten to withdraw them should the local authority not use the staff in the manner intended.

Because of its relative newness the health centre is still in an experimental stage and its effectiveness as a comprehensive centre for all aspects of health varies from one district to another. One of the centres we visited appeared to be functioning more as a cottage hospital or maternity unit than as a general health centre for the area. Transport is so difficult in many rural areas that the centre can rarely be used as a reference service for dispensaries which may lie ten or twenty miles away across open country. For patients in the immediate area, the rural health centre provides a better service than that given in rural dispensaries: in particular, consultation at the centre is normally with a medical assistant.

Consultations at one of the 350 Grade 'A' dispensaries run by local authorities are usually with a two-year trained rural medical aid, while the 365 Grade 'B' dispensaries are usually staffed by a dresser, who has learnt his practice through a somewhat casual apprenticeship in a hospital. Rural dispensary services are also under the general supervision of central government medical staff. But the shortage of doctors and other staff, the pressure of other work and poor—in some cases non-existent—communications make effective supervision of the work of all rural medical aids and dressers impossible to attain. The health centres are provided with Land-Rovers by UNICEF. Few of the other dispensaries have either motorized transport, telephone or radio, and many are not served by all-weather roads. Seriously ill patients have to be transported to hospitals by litter, by tradesman's lorry or by one of the Land-Rovers attached to the few health centres. Such help may have to be summoned by a relative who may make the journey by bicycle or on foot.

About 6·5 million new attendances were recorded in health centres and dispensaries in 1961. Total attendances numbered over 12 million. Consultations were given by thirty-four medical assistants, 368 rural medical aids and 723 dressers. About 1,800 beds are maintained in small units attached to local authority dispensaries and health centres. These are intended as 'holding beds' for acute illness or patients awaiting transfer. Maternity and child welfare clinics under the control of local authorities saw some 69,000 mothers and 53,000 children (first attendances) in 1961 and supervised over 22,000 confinements.

The rural health services provided by the local authorities have been expanding rapidly in response to the demand for more medical attention and maternity and child welfare services. Expenditure on these services by local authorities has risen from £37,000 in 1946 to almost £700,000 in 1961. The trends in expenditure and utilization are shown in Table VIII.

Table VIII

Expenditure and Utilization of
Local Authority Medical Services: 1946/61

Year	No. of first attendances (thousands)			Expenditure £'000
	Ante-natal clinics	Child health clinics	Dispen-saries	
1946	2·4*	0·5*	1,450	37
1951	6·7	3·0	1,992	92
1956	19·8	13·8	3,345	280
1961	68·6	52·6	6,506	699

*1947 figures as those for 1946 are not available.

Although there is no common policy, charges are not generally imposed at local authority dispensaries and clinics. Less than twenty of the fifty-six local treasuries record any income from medical services. Any income that is recorded is usually very small and is derived from various sources, including charges for drugs, treatment of venereal disease and in one district charges to non-Africans for dispensary services. All these charges only added up to about £6,000 in 1961.

There are thus very few financial restrictions, in the form of charges imposed by local and central government, on the growing demand for medical care in the rural areas. This demand, understandable enough when viewed in the context of the low standards of health and nutrition and reinforced as a result of mass education, is expressed by the activities of local self-help schemes. In some areas these schemes are resulting in the raising of environmental standards; in others, in the construction of new dispensaries without the guarantee of trained staff to run them. In one area we learnt of thirty new dispensaries, built hopefully through self-help schemes, which were standing empty and unused. It is sad to see so much community self-help being frustrated. This problem is, we understand, fully appreciated by the leaders of the community development movement. In later chapters we return to the need to bring closer together the local health services and self-help activities of many kinds.

So far as there are any clear distinctions to be drawn at the present time between central and local government health services they are geographical rather than functional. Central government, to quote the words of the Chief Medical Officer, 'provides a direct service to the population down to the level of the district and sub-district hospitals'. People in the rural areas, however, 'for their hospital services ... depend upon the small rural dispensaries maintained by the local authorities and upon the slowly increasing number of health centres'.[9]

The functions and responsibilities of local government in

[9] Clyde, D. F. 'Epilogue', *History of the Medical Services of Tanganyika*, Dar es Salaam, 1962.

Tanganyika have been the subject of a recent report by the City Treasurer of Nairobi.[10] In this report, Mr. Kent suggests that local authorities should extend their functions as providers of medical care to include the district hospitals, which they would take over from central government and for which they would receive government grants-in-aid. If his recommendations were accepted, the district council would then directly control all the medical care provided by the public sector in its administrative area. His report has, however, little to say about the role of the voluntary agencies which make a considerable contribution to the medical services of the rural areas.

Voluntary Agency Medical Services
At the end of 1961, there were forty-eight voluntary hospitals with resident doctors (4,724 beds), sixty-four dispensaries with more than twenty beds (2,905 beds) and 175 other bedded dispensaries (721 beds). The voluntary agencies dealt with a similar volume of maternity and child health work to that of local authorities; in their 137 ante-natal clinics and 190 child health clinics almost 60,000 mothers and over 54,000 children were seen in 1961 and nearly 22,000 confinements were attended by their staff. More nurses and midwives are trained at voluntary hospitals than in government training schools. In 1961, 105 nurses and forty-five midwives qualified from voluntary training centres, compared with thirty-nine nurses and thirty-five midwives in central government centres. There are also voluntary agency schools for training medical assistants, rural medical aids and village midwives.

Although 43% of all in-patients are accommodated in voluntary hospitals or dispensaries few of the voluntary hospitals have any formal links with the government services. At least twenty-one separate voluntary agencies operate medical services in Tanganyika. The number and variety of these agencies present many difficult problems of developing an integrated service. There is no central organization to

---

[10] Kent, A. W. *Report on the Services to be Administered by Local Authorities in Tanganyika and the Consequential Financial Arrangements*, 1962.

which these agencies owe allegiance; individual hospitals are supervised by their own parent organization. There is little co-ordination, either among the voluntary agencies themselves or between the voluntary agencies and the public sector. A Mission Medical Advisory Committee exists to foster medical co-ordination centrally, between representatives of the agencies and representatives of the government, but the decisions of this body are in no way binding on individual agencies. Recently the central government has tried to encourage closer co-ordination—chiefly by using the grants paid to the voluntary agencies.

The central government has been assisting these agencies with grants since the Second World War. Grants totalled £550 in 1938; they now run to over £150,000 a year. These are paid out according to regulations laid down by government, most recently revised in 1955. About three-fifths of the voluntary institutions receive grants; the remaining two-fifths are ineligible or do not wish to apply. Generally it is the smaller hospitals and dispensaries which are not grant-aided. At the end of December 1960, 1,776 beds were not grant-aided out of a total of 7,512 beds. In addition, central government pays grants to agencies for leprosy cases and for the maintenance of mental patients, and provides free drugs for the treatment of leprosy and tuberculosis.

The main subsidy to voluntary agencies is, however, the grant system to general hospitals. The total sum paid was £152,000 in 1961/62. Grants are payable under three heads: staff grants, training grants and additional (or bed) grants.

Staff grants, which account for almost two-thirds of the total grants, are payable on three conditions. First, the medical unit must in the view of the Ministry 'fulfil an acknowledged need' in the area. Second, it must maintain an adequate standard of building and equipment. Third, it must employ what the government considers to be an adequate number of qualified staff. All hospitals in receipt of these grants must have a resident qualified medical practitioner. In addition to these conditions, the agencies themselves have to find from their own funds not less than

50% of the value of staff grants. The grants are payable in the form of a lump sum for each member of staff in a defined category up to a stated maximum number of such staff. These sums are set out in Table IX and range from one-quarter to one-half of the equivalent government starting salary,[11] and would be a smaller proportion of the average government salary.

The maximum number of staff for whom grants are payable varies according to the size of the hospital. For example, a hospital with twenty to forty-nine beds is allowed one doctor, two nurses or midwives registered in part 'A' of the Tanganyika Register, two medical, laboratory or pharmaceutical assistants, and a number of nurses or midwives registered in part 'B' calculated at the ratio of one nurse to eight beds.

Training grants are payable in the form of a lump sum for each student qualifying. This varies from £90 for a health nurse to £180 for a medical assistant. In addition, a lump sum of £250 a year is payable for a newly established school until it is possible for students to qualify from it.

'Additional' grants are paid according to the number of beds approved for this purpose by the Chief Medical Officer. Since the avowed aim of the government is to have one hospital bed per thousand of the population in each district, these bed grants are payable for all approved beds in voluntary hospitals up to a total (including government beds) of 1 bed per 1,000 population in the district. The level of grant varies according to specified conditions. In an administrative district where there are no government in-patient facilities the sum of £20 is paid per approved voluntary agency bed. Smaller grants are paid where government hospitals do exist, depending on the bed ratio attained by the government facilities. For example, in a district in which government hospitals provide less than 0·3 beds per 1,000 population, a bed grant of £10 per approved bed up to 1 bed per 1,000 population is payable to voluntary hospitals in the same district. No bed grant is payable to a

---

[11] Taken from the figures given in the Adu Report (*Report of Tanganyika Salaries Commission, 1961*).

Table IX

Staff Grants Payable to Approved Voluntary Hospitals with Resident Medical Practitioners

	Grant £	Scale	Starting salary £	Grant as percentage of starting salary
Registered medical practitioner . .	450	AP2-3	1,158	39
Licensed medical practitioner . .	300	TO3-4	702	43
Registered nurse tutor . .	300	TO4-5	894	34
Registered nurse part 'A' . .	200	TO2	444	45
Registered midwife part 'A' . .	120	TO2	444	27
Nurse/midwife part 'A' . .	275	TO2	444	62
Registered nurse part 'B' . .	80	MT	174	46
Registered midwife part 'B' . .	60	MT	174	34
Nurse/midwife part 'B' . .	95	MT	183	52
Medical assistant, laboratory assistant, pharmaceutical assistant . .	125	TO1-1A	219-300	42-57
Rural medical aid . .	75	MT	174	43
Health nurse . .	35	MT	174	20

general hospital which offers no training facilities and is within fifty miles of a district hospital where there are already over 0·8 beds per 1,000 population.

In general, the system of grants is intended to encourage voluntary agencies to locate their facilities where they are most needed and to undertake the training of staff. There is no financial incentive to undertake preventive work unless it is part of some training scheme. It is only recently that any voluntary agencies have become interested in entering this field. In one district, for example, a health team consisting of a public health nurse and two assistants is sent out from a mission hospital to do tuberculin testing in the local schools and administer BCG vaccine supplied by the local authority where it is needed. Such public health work is still only rarely undertaken by a voluntary agency.

Government grants-in-aid represent an important part of the total income of the voluntary hospitals. The exact proportion is not known but we estimate it at between 20 and 40%. Another considerable source of income comes from patients' fees. Unlike government, the voluntary agencies generally charge fees for all patients seen, either as in-patients or as out-patients: moreover, food is not normally provided for patients in voluntary hospitals. Emergency cases are seen without question but 'cold' cases, and those where there is thought to be no urgency, are advised to save their money until they can afford to pay the fee, or are referred as non-paying patients to the nearest government hospital or dispensary.

It seems that there are three main reasons why the agencies impose charges. First, it is thought that patients ought to pay something if they can. Second, the existence of charges was said to control the demand on the hospitals' limited facilities and thereby helped to maintain standards for those who used them. At one hospital which we visited, only thirty to sixty patients a day were seen; whereas only a few miles away a government centre was overwhelmed with between 200 and 300 patients a day, seen without charge. Third, many of the voluntary agencies are forced to charge to make ends meet. One agency told us that half their income came from charges to patients and that without these charges they would have to close down their beds. The sums charged vary from hospital to hospital. One hospital we visited charged twenty cents per out-patient visit, with additional charges for the more expensive drugs, and twenty shillings per in-patient admission together with fees for particular services as laid down in a fee schedule. Fees are not standardized between one agency and another. Since fees represent the most flexible item in the income of most agencies they tend to vary according to the policy of the institution and its financial position.

No information is available on the amount of income which the missionary societies receive from abroad in the form of money or goods. We were told that cash income from abroad is used primarily for building projects and equipment and not generally to defray ordinary running expenses. Again this may well vary considerably between one agency and another.

Donated services are common to all voluntary agencies. They form a 'hidden saving' in the overall budget. For example, one agency was able to employ eight expatriate doctors in its hospitals in 1961/62 for £5,800 including an allowance for their quarters and contributions to a pension scheme. Another agency pays one of its doctors only £300 a year. Where expatriate nurses are also employed a very considerable reduction can be made in the total expenditure of the hospital, compared with the government hospital which is committed to salary scales and regular increments and also to substantial additional allowances in respect of expatriates. Another important source of saving is represented by lower wages and salaries paid to locally recruited subordinate staff, and a third takes the form of a higher proportion of student nurses and midwives. For these reasons it is probably true that voluntary agencies as they are now constituted are able to provide equivalent patient services somewhat more cheaply than the government. No figures are, however, available to substantiate or refute this argument, or to indicate whether conditions are changing.

Grant-aided hospitals are required to submit simple

annual accounts to the Ministry of Health giving details of expenditure on staff, buildings, equipment and supplies, and training. No parallel data are available for non grant-aided hospitals. The Mission Medical Advisory Committee includes representatives from grant-aided agencies only, and there is at present no formal communication between the Ministry and non grant-aided voluntary agencies. Thus, it is impossible to estimate with any accuracy the work and cost of the voluntary medical services as a whole.

The Cost of Medical Care

In financial terms, the central government has for a long time been the largest provider of medical care. In 1961/62, central government spent almost £2·4 million on recurrent health expenditure and a further £338,000 on capital works. This combined sum represented about 8 % of the total government budget. Local government, with a budget which has been expanding rapidly, spent approximately £800,000 in the calendar year 1961—almost twice the corresponding expenditure of 1955. Most of this sum (£699,000) was spent by local authorities on the rural health services, provided through their twenty-two rural health centres and 715 dispensaries. The remaining amount (£102,000) was spent by town councils and by the City Council of Dar es Salaam, primarily on urban public health services. Thus the public sector of the economy (central and local government) accounted for a total expenditure on health of some £3·2 million in the fiscal year 1961/62—an outlay of about seven shillings per head of the population.

These are the only figures on health service expenditure that it is possible to estimate with any accuracy. No reliable figures are available for the cost of the voluntary medical services, but we estimate, on the basis of a sample analysis of voluntary hospital budgets, that their total annual expenditure is now running at somewhere between half a million and one million pounds. This expenditure by voluntary agencies was partly financed by grants of over £150,000 a year by the government for approved hospitals and training services. The voluntary agencies provide

67

almost half of the medically supervised beds in general hospitals. The staff of these agencies sees one in nine of all out-patients (see Table II). These voluntary agency medical services add appreciably to the country's total expenditure on health. Moreover, in estimating this contribution it has to be remembered that some of those working in voluntary hospitals and dispensaries accept remuneration for their services which is substantially below the salaries paid in government service.

Similarly, it is only possible to guess at the expenditure on health through the industrial health services.[12] Approximately 11% of all in-patient admissions and 7% of all out-patient first attendances are accounted for by industrial health facilities. According to the available industrial health service staff figures it seems likely that these add a sum of about £150,000 to the national total of health expenditure.

From these tentative figures, it appears that the total of

Table X

*Expenditure on Health by
Organized Health Services—Tanganyika, 1961*

	£'000
Central Government:	
Recurrent	2,395
Capital	338
Local Government:	
Town Councils	102
Other Authorities	699
Voluntary Agencies (net.) . . .	600
Industrial Health	150
Total Expenditure:	£4,284

[12] 'Industrial health services' in this context include all health services paid for by employers, whether on sisal estates, in mines or in factories.

current and capital expenditure on health services by 'organized' services in Tanganyika amounts to about £4·3 million divided as shown in Table X.

This total of about £4·3 million represents 2·3% of the gross domestic product, or a little under ten shillings per head per year. In addition to this expenditure on organized services, there is private expenditure incurred on three different types of practice—'western', traditional and illicit.

The Private Sector

It was estimated by the Medical Department at the end of 1961 that about 180 out of the 400 'western' trained doctors in Tanganyika were then engaged in private practice, and that no less than 130 out of this 180 resided in five urban areas—Dar es Salaam, Tanga, Arusha, Moshi and Mwanza, with a combined population of 200,000 people. Private practitioners naturally gravitate to concentrations of population and concentrations of relative wealth where the government hospital service is also concentrated. In a country with extreme contrasts of health care—like Tanganyika—this tendency accentuates the gulf between life in the towns and life in the rural areas.

There are many private practitioners who provide a service which is of a standard comparable to that typically available in Europe or America. However, the undesirable practice of charging for treatment and not for advice has developed, and many practitioners who do not like the system see themselves forced to operate it by competitive pressures. Some of these pressures come from patients themselves. As a result of the success of modern methods of treatment of yaws and certain other diseases, health has come to be regarded as a matter of being injected when sick rather than of adopting radical changes in diet and personal habits.

Thus, private medical practice in East Africa is now subject to demands which set a high premium on the sale of useless and sometimes dangerous injections, frequently involving the misuse of antibiotic and other modern remedies. Drug-resistant tuberculosis is already a serious problem, both from a treatment and a public health point of view. Unethical and potentially harmful activities—treatment without examination, misuse of drugs, and even improper extraction of fees—are not confined to the private sector of the profession. In the public service auxiliary medical workers in clinics and dispensaries, with little or no supervision, are particularly exposed to these temptations and pressures in situations of heavy and growing demand for medical attention.

We do not wish to enlarge on these matters here, beyond calling attention to the fact that they are all part of the general problem of improving the quantity and quality of medical care in Tanganyika. They encourage wrong attitudes to health and disease; they do not call for a positive and preventive response from patients; they may lead to abuse of the hospital and public services; they are economically wasteful; and they must inevitably lead in time to a decline in the doctor's clinical powers of diagnosis and therapy.

These questions are no doubt receiving serious examination by the medical profession. But they are also of concern to the government which is seeking to encourage attitudes of self-help and prevention. Moreover, the high incomes which can be earned in private practice, whether ethical or unethical, may attract doctors away from the public services, and tend also to concentrate more doctors in the urban areas to the further neglect of the rural population. The government is therefore forced to pay more if it wishes to retain its doctors in competition with these forms of private practice. Thus, it can employ fewer doctors. In situations of rapid social and technical change it is understandable that these pressures should develop. It must be recorded, however, that there are many practitioners and medical workers in Tanganyika who attempt, in the face of serious deficiencies in resources, to put the needs of their patients first.

In a public statement in the National Assembly in December 1961, the then Minister of Health and Labour proposed that doctors in private practice should be required in future to obtain a licence for which a 'substantial fee' would be charged and that all private practitioners intending to work in Tanganyika should in future serve for a number of years in the government or voluntary agency services. 'In the rural areas,' he said in justification of these proposals, 'the choice is between one doctor or no doctor, and,' he continued, 'we cannot afford the luxury of extreme contrast in the towns.' When pressed for a definition of a 'substantial fee', he mentioned the figure of £100 per month, payable to the government by each private practitioner as a licence fee for his continuing in private practice. This proposal was not well received in certain quarters and the matter was referred to a committee, set up at the beginning of 1962, to take evidence from interested parties and to consider the possible implications of the suggested measures. This committee has not yet reported.

Private accommodation for in-patients exists only in Dar es Salaam, Moshi and Arusha. Little is known about these private hospitals or nursing homes as no register is kept. There are three nursing homes in Dar es Salaam, of which two have over twenty beds. Additional expenditure on medical care is incurred through the country's twenty pharmaceutical shops. Nine of these are in Dar es Salaam : there are four towns which have two pharmacists' shops, and three which have one shop. There are thus only eight centres in the whole country to which a patient can take a private doctor's prescription for a preparation subject to legal restriction. We were told, however, that some preparations can in practice be obtained by a persistent patient, with or without a prescription, from general stores that are to be found in many parts of the country.

Private dental practice is also to be found in Tanganyika. Of the thirty dentists registered to practice at the end of 1961, nineteen were thought to be engaged in private practice. It is not known, however, how many of these nineteen are actually resident or currently practising.

The traditional practice of medicine by *bona fide* medicine men 'recognized by the community to which they belong to be duly trained in such practice' is specifically provided for in the Medical Practitioners and Dentists Ordinance.[13]

[13] Medical Practitioners and Dentists Ordinance, Cap. 409, Supp. 59, S. 37.

Provided life is not thereby endangered, the medicine man may use whatever remedies he chooses without the supervision of a Western-trained doctor. There is extremely little published information which indicates the extent, methods or efficacy of traditional medicine in Tanganyika.[14] We were told that traditional practice by herbalists is to be found in every settlement. In many cases patients come to hospitals or clinics as a last resort after traditional medicine has failed. There are also medicine men who provide treatment for certain psychological or psycho-somatic conditions which is said to be remarkably effective. There is no formal link between government and traditional practitioners, or between the latter and the organized health services. It is not possible to make any quantitative estimate of the work done or to estimate total expenditure incurred on these services.

In addition to legal private practice, Western and traditional, there is a certain amount of illicit practice by unqualified persons. Most of them have previously been employed as auxiliaries in the organized services. They thereby acquired an acquaintance with Western methods of treatment (if not of diagnosis) and local prestige essential for 'successful' practice. For obvious reasons we have been unable to ascertain the extent of such illicit practices but we were told that they did not constitute a major problem at the present time.

Staffing the Services

The number of professional staff registered in Tanganyika is set out in Table XI. The year 1956 is inserted as a guide to manpower trends.

These figures, especially those for doctors, dentists, medical assistants and nurses, must be read with caution as the register may include a number who do not practise or who have left the country. There were only 403 registered and licensed medical practitioners *resident and practising* in Tanganyika in 1961 : 182 were in private practice, 140 in

---

[14] For some illustrations and examples see Wilcocks, C. *Aspects of Medical Investigation in Africa*, Oxford University Press, 1962.

Table XI

Staff numbers as at 31st December 1956 and 1961*

	1956	1961
Registered Medical Practitioners	385	549
Private practice . . .	175	303
Other	210	246
Licensed Medical Practitioners	54	31
Private practice . . .	14	18
Other	40	13
Registered Dentists . .	26	30
Private practice . . .	17	19
Other	9	11
Licensed Dentists . . .	2 ⎫	not
Private practice . . .	1 ⎬	available
Other	1 ⎭	
Medical Assistants . . .	200	402
Pharmaceutical Assistants .	25	38
Laboratory Assistants . .	43	49
Dental Assistants . . .	—	19
Radiographers . . .	3	2
Radiological Technician . .	—	1
Mental Nurses . . .	11	12
Registered Nurses . . .	1,024	1,999
Registered Midwives . .	—	905†
Laboratory Technologists .	3	3
Pharmacists	25	50

*In general, these are cumulative totals as yearly registrations are not required.

†Some midwives are also included in the figures for nurses.

Source: Ministry of Health and Labour, as submitted to the Statistical Abstract, 1962.

government service, and eighty-one were employed by the voluntary medical services. Some of the private practitioners are also employed as industrial medical officers. Not only are most of the private practitioners concentrated in the towns but the doctors employed by the central government are also mostly stationed in the towns, since the government hospitals to which they are attached are sited there. Voluntary agency doctors, on the other hand, are more likely to be found in the rural areas where traditionally the church hospitals and dispensaries have been established.

The changes in the numbers of trained staff since 1956 have been important. There was a small increase in the number of medical practitioners engaged in the public and voluntary sectors between 1956 and 1961—but hardly enough to keep pace with the growth of population. As regards the nursing services, there was a striking expansion over the five-year period in the number of trained nurses. The absolute increase was nearly 1,000—or nearly double. By contrast, despite increased demand, there has been little increase in laboratory and X-ray staff.

3   The Health Needs of Tanganyika

Many of the medical problems of Tanganyika are largely dictated by its geographical and demographic characteristics. Within its boundaries, there are extremes of height, temperature and vegetation. Out of the total area of 365,000 square miles, one-third is uninhabited, much of it because of inadequate rainfall or tsetse infestation. Over about a quarter of the country, rainfall is less than thirty inches each year. Even where the annual rainfall is greater, the dry season can be severe. As a result, parts of the country are often subjected to either drought or flood, both of which can lead to famine.

In only a tenth of the country does the population density exceed ten to the square mile, but there are within these areas pockets of population where more than 100 or even 200 people live in each square mile. There are twenty small towns with populations of five to fifteen thousand, surrounded by closely settled agricultural populations, to a radius of about fifty miles. In the two cities of Tanga (40,000) and Dar es Salaam (130,000) are to be found all the environmental problems of town-life anywhere in the world. This already varied picture is further complicated by the special development areas, such as that of the Rufiji project, of which there are likely to be more in future. These particular areas require special consideration, as also does the less organized settlement of farmers or groups of farmers on previously uncultivated land.

A medical programme must aim to cater for all these

different types of population settlement. The attempt to provide even territorial coverage faces formidable physical difficulties in the sparsely populated areas. These areas are, however, important. The people in them, or migrating to them, are subject to special health risks; they require protection as much as—or indeed more than—those in more populated parts of the country. Progress will depend on the provision of water supplies and on the development of all-weather transport and communications, as much as on improvements in health and other social services.

Any plan for the health services must also take account of the pattern of disease, the present and future age structure of the population, and of wider questions of economic and social development.

Tanganyika is constantly exposed to the risk of epidemic outbreaks which can disrupt the life of the community under attack. That epidemic diseases do not now figure greatly in the pattern of morbidity and mortality is perhaps the most notable achievement of the medical services. Nevertheless, these diseases remain a risk that can only be kept in check by the exercise of continual vigilance. Smallpox, typhoid, whooping cough, measles, cerebro-spinal meningitis and poliomyelitis are prevalent over a wide area; more localized hazards are plague, trypanosomiasis, typhus and rabies; other intermittent visitors are influenza and insect-borne virus infections such as the newly recognized Chikungunya and O'nyong nyong fevers.

Among all these, smallpox is kept relatively under control by vaccination, but trypanosomiasis has occurred in devastating epidemics since it entered Tanganyika in virulent form forty years ago; freedom from recurrence cannot be assured without continued observation and active measures of control. Plague has occurred on a relatively minor scale, but remains endemic in the wild rodent population. Whooping cough and measles are important contributors to child mortality; in other parts of Africa the latter is counted among the major killing diseases. Poliomyelitis has only recently begun to change its behaviour from endemic to epidemic form; there is reason to expect frequent and severe epidemics in the future.

Epidemic control requires a standing organization which can ensure that all possible routine measures are taken to prevent and limit outbreaks, and which maintains continuous observation to facilitate early recognition and control. Such an organization must have sufficient flexibility to anticipate and identify events which cannot be foreseen long in advance.

A second aspect of the disease pattern is the prevalence in all age groups of a load of chronic endemic infections, parasitic diseases and impaired nutrition, which although they may not all carry a high specific mortality in adults, exact a toll, particularly in anaemia and digestive disorders, reflected in poor physical development and physical and mental lassitude, detracting greatly from the well-being, efficiency and general enjoyment of life of large numbers of the population and contributing indirectly to the shortening of life. Of these, malaria, hookworm, tuberculosis and venereal disease are the most widespread; bilharzia, roundworm, amoebic infection and filariasis in its various forms are more locally distributed. Trachoma and ophthalmia account for much eye disease, particularly among the pastoral tribes living in fly-infested kraals. Most of these, again, are diseases whose causes are known and preventable, but the application of effective preventive measures presents a staggering problem which has to be considered in the context of social, educational and economic resources.

A third aspect of the disease pattern is one that is partly obscured by those already described. The common worldwide diseases of the heart, chest, digestive and urinary tracts, nervous and other systems of the body, including cancer in many of its forms, may be as prevalent and fatal in Tanganyika as anywhere else. Much more needs to be known about the extent of these problems and of the incidence of mental disorder and psychoneurosis, which together may account for a large proportion of the country's ill health. Successful control of the 'tropical' diseases will bring all these conditions into increasing prominence. The challenge facing the Health Service will alter correspondingly, as has happened within one or two generations in other parts of the world.

A major obstacle to precise assessment of priorities in the country's health needs is the absence of accurate morbidity data and vital statistics. There have been careful studies at East African hospitals[1,2,3] which reveal the picture in kind but not in quantity. These figures reflect the prevalence of diseases for which some people are admitted to hospital and therefore understate the prevalence of others. Moreover, they reflect the situation only in a particular locality. Returns from rural centres, on the other hand, reflect the common infections and minor illnesses which auxiliary medical staff are able to recognize, but again they understate serious and often fatal diseases which go undiagnosed. Tuberculosis,[4] leprosy,[5] and trypanosomiasis[6] have been the subject of field surveys and are better documented. Surveys such as those of Usborne[7] and Evans[8] are examples of broader field studies. A cancer survey[9] in Uganda is yielding important data related to a local population census which may be relevant to Tanganyika. These account for only a small fraction of the information wanted and emphasize the need for broad based epidemiological and population studies.

[1] Shaper, A. G. and Shaper, L. J. 'Analysis of Medical Admissions to Mulago Hospital, 1957' *East African Medical Journal*, 1958, **35**, 647.
[2] Musoke, L. J. 'An Analysis of Admissions to the Paediatric Division of Mulago Hospital in 1959' *Archives of Diseases of Children* 1961, **36**, 305.
[3] Turner, P. P. 'The Pattern of Disease as seen by Medical Admissions to the Coast Province General Hospital in 1960'—*East African Medical Journal*, 1962, **39**, 121.
[4] World Health Organization, Tuberculosis Research Office. *A Tuberculosis Survey in Tanganyika*, Copenhagen, 1958.
[5] Innes, J. R., 'Leprosy in Tanganyika: Surveys of Lake Province, Southern Highlands Province, Southern Province *East African Medical Journal*, 1949, **26**, 199 and 212, 1950, **27**, 459.
[6] Sleeping Sickness Service, unpublished Annual Reports to the Medical Department.
[7] Usborne, V. 'Home and Dispensary Findings in a Survey of Wasukuma Children', *East African Medical Journal*, 1954, **31**, 531.
[8] Evans, W. J. M., 'A Survey of a Tropical Area . . . Health Problems Associated with Resettlement', *Journal of the Royal Sanitary Institute*, 1950, **70**, 449.
[9] Davies, J. N. P., Wilson, B. A., Knowleden, J., 'Cancer Incidence of the African Population of Kyadondo (Uganda)', *Lancet* 1962, **2**, 328.

Population trends are discussed in Chapter 4. What concerns us here is the age structure of the population for whom health services need to be provided. Nearly half of Tanganyika's nine-and-a-half million people are children under fifteen, and by far the largest age group is that of infancy. The population pyramid tapers rapidly after early middle life: there are few old people. This pattern is not unusual for a community with grossly inadequate environmental hygiene and low levels of living. High mortality in infancy continues into early childhood and results in the death of 30 to 50% of children before they reach maturity. Mortality in later years is less excessive, though still relatively high by European standards.

No data are available upon which to base firm conclusions on the causes of this high infant and child mortality. Hospital studies cannot represent the situation in the population at large. Most infant deaths occur at home, unrecorded and undiagnosed. But we have no reason to disagree with the belief which is generally held that malaria, acute gastro-intestinal infections, malnutrition and pneumonia are the most important contributors at this age. Children are born without the immunity to malaria which those who survive it acquire (though at the price of much chronic anaemia and debility). Ignorance and the force of custom, as well as poverty, contribute to fatal malnutrition. Measles, whooping cough and other infections contribute to the incidence of fatal pneumonia. Intestinal infections which cause acute but transient dysentery in an adult can be rapidly fatal in a baby without skilled medical care.

The social, economic and educational aspects of these problems need not be enlarged upon here. All are changing and it is upon wider education, improved methods of agriculture and greater wealth that solutions will depend, as much as upon the direct application of scientific knowledge within the health services.

The history, the achievements and some of the present limitations of medical care and public health activity in Tanganyika have been discussed in Chapters 1 and 2. It would be unwise and inappropriate, even if it were feasible,

79

to transport to Tanganyika an entirely western pattern of health services. For efficiency and economy, the services must meet the special needs of the people in their local circumstances. Priorities must then be indicated by the analysis of these needs. Much will also depend on the manpower or skills available and locally acquired. It is important to recognize that it is the circumstances and environment, rather than the particular ills to which the people are prone, that make the contrast between so much ill health in Tanganyika and better health in western countries. It is necessary to build a health service adaptable to these varied conditions, which must, for a considerable time, make the most economical use it can of scarce skills, while endeavouring to bring the greatest benefit to as large a proportion of the population as possible.

Community and social development must play an important part in this field; first in the creation of awareness of the possibility of improvement and the stimulation of initiative to achieve it, and later in evoking support for the administrative and financial measures which become necessary. These basic educational processes lead on, once they are established, to the more traditional forms of technological teaching and applied services in relation to health.

The organization of a system of vital statistics is necessary to provide the fundamental basis for the detailed planning of health development and the rational distribution of activities in different parts of the country. They also play the important role of supplying material for the stimulation of public interest and of the awareness of the need for betterment, together with an appreciation of the results of remedial action when it is taken. Registration of the facts of birth and death can be initiated in a society without much medical aid, though certification of the causes of death cannot be generally enforced until medical practitioners are adequately distributed throughout the entire country.

The aims of a health service are to help to bring about a healthy society, free from the risks of epidemic disease, in which the individual can attain and enjoy the full physical and mental development open to him, and has a reasonable prospect of survival through childhood and normal adult years, free from the incubus of infection or preventable disorder and able to obtain medical aid when he needs it.

The chief developments required now towards meeting Tanganyika's health needs may be enumerated on the following lines. They include measures of broad application directed to general betterment and improved knowledge of problems and methods, not all of them the responsibility of a Ministry of Health (the indirect attack); and those of more particular application (the direct attack). The order of enumeration is not intended to indicate priorities, which are discussed in other chapters.

The Indirect Attack

Provision of rural domestic water supplies on a much larger scale—where necessary by boreholes, dams, etc.

Extension of piped water supplies and waterborne sanitation.

Extension and improvement of all-weather communications.

Education, including adult education channelled through community development agencies, in food production (crops, fish and animal protein); on man and his environment in relation to health; on personal and domestic hygiene and prophylaxis; on mental health.

Registration of births and deaths.

Establishment of a central unit for the study of disease incidence, distribution and trends, both epidemic and endemic.

Development of medical research, independently and in co-operation with the University and the Common Services organizations and international research foundations.

The Direct Attack

The development of environmental public health activities as a separate whole-time service closely associated with local government and adult education and community development activities; separate from but co-operating with the personal medical services.

81

The education of parents in matters of child health and up-bringing, through the medium of community development agencies and Health Centres working in co-operation.

Extension of personal medical services for cure, care and education, with emphasis on the development of a system of Health Units operating in both rural and urban areas, located in such a way as to bring these services within reach of all.

Extension of midwifery, ante-natal and child-welfare facilities, and especially of domiciliary midwifery, in association with the Health Units.

Consolidation and extension of the hospital service, with the emphasis on fewer hospitals of larger size equipped and staffed for effective support of the Health Units.

Preparatory work to develop the conditions for specific disease eradication campaigns to be undertaken when a general network of Health Units is satisfactorily established, and the environmental services sufficiently expanded to meet the WHO 'pre-eradication' criteria.

4 The Economics of
Health and Population in 1980

The health needs of Tanganyika, briefly reviewed in the previous chapter, obviously demand far-reaching improvements in the health services. More and more people are, at the same time, becoming aware of what better health could mean to them and to their children. They are seeing medical care—like better food, education, water supplies, roads and other necessities—as one of the ways by which they may lead fuller lives as citizens of their country.

We must, therefore, also take account, in drawing up a plan for the future of the health services which will reflect the wishes of the people, of all these other needs which form part of the demand for a better standard of living. It would be no service to produce a report, however splendidly designed, that called for the impossible. It would be a disservice to ignore these many other tasks to which Tanganyika has set her hands.

We had, therefore, at the beginning, to ask ourselves what were the probable limits to expenditure by government on the health services during the next twenty years. Only by asking this question could we realistically consider the problem of priorities between health services and other needs, between investing in prevention and self-help and investing in curative services, between hospitals in urban areas and first-line services in the rural areas. Each of these different claims calls also for more trained and educated men and women to staff the services. Again, we had to set these claims for trained staff against the claims from other sectors of the economy and the probable future supply of educated young people from a developing educational system.

Finally, we had to ask ourselves how many people would be needing health services during the next twenty years. Another five million people by 1980—and mostly children and young people—could clearly make a very great difference to any plan for the health services in the future. At the end of this chapter we therefore consider various estimates of population growth.

Our first chapter, in which we surveyed the history of the health services, illustrated forcibly the importance of taking account of these economic questions. We displayed a veritable graveyard of health plans. On each occasion the Treasury seems to have been responsible by rejecting, obstructing or quietly burying them. We have to appreciate, however, that behind the actions of the Treasury there have been forces at work which no economist, let alone health planner, however realistic, could be expected to predict— the world depression of the thirties, the general fall of commodity prices in the fifties, and the effects of the dramatic political changes in Tanganyika in the late fifties and early sixties. This history shows that earlier health plans have been disrupted more by economic forces than by new techniques of health planning, advances in medicine or new theories of health administration.

In drawing up our plan we have thus had to look at the *whole* economy to assess the part which health services are likely to be asked to play in any wider plan for national development. Tanganyika has not yet had time, however, to devise such a broader programme nor to establish the necessary planning agencies. There is a short-term plan in existence which expires in 1963/64 but, as yet, there is no longer-term plan. We understand that the Government is setting up a permanent agency whose task it will be to plan for longer ahead. But the completion of our report could not await the findings of this body.

The long-term economic prospects of Tanganyika may appear to be a somewhat remote subject for a medical mission to explore. In one respect, however, the subject is specially relevant to our terms of reference. The level of living of the people of Tanganyika does not only depend upon what is produced : it depends also on the number of producers and consumers. We have already referred to the heavy toll which disease and malnutrition take of human life and their disabling effects which reduce activity and output. A radical reduction in premature death must be one of the objects of any plan for health, but the consequence may be to make still harder the task of producers in raising the level of living of the average citizen. We give special attention to this subject because the recent economic survey mission[1] completed its report of over three hundred pages on a balanced programme of social and economic development without alluding at any stage to the question of future population trends.

On the recent rate of economic growth the report stated that 'although national income statistics are only available from 1954 on, it seems possible to assert that from 1948 to 1958 the economy as a whole grew at an annual rate of at least 5%.'[2] Up to 1960, this rate of growth continued at about the same rate : over the six years from 1955 to 1960, the gross domestic product increased by about 4·6% per annum in money terms.[2] But in 1961 this rate of progress was not maintained. The gross domestic product in money terms increased by only 0·4%,[4] making an average rate of growth of about 4% for the whole seven-year period *in money terms*.

No general price index is at present maintained. There is, however, a Retail Price Index of Goods Consumed by Wage-Earners in Dar es Salaam. This index increased by about 10% between the beginning of 1956 and the end of 1961.[5] It is therefore possible that over the past seven years the national income in *real terms* has been increasing by little more than the recent rate of growth of population,

[1] The International Bank of Reconstruction and Development, *The Economic Development of Tanganyika*, Dar es Salaam, 1960.
[2] *ibid.* p. 14.
[3] *Budget Survey, 1961/62*, p. 2.
[4] *Budget Survey, 1962/63*, p. 2.
[5] *Budget Survey, 1961/62*, p. 13 and *1962/63* p. 17.

85

which we take to be about 2% per annum.[6] The Budget Survey published in 1962 envisaged that the end of 1962 would show no increase of production in real terms over 1960.[7] Thus, real income per head may have been lower in 1962 than in 1960.

As regards the immediate future, the short-term development plan (1961/62 to 1963/64) took the recent rate of growth to be 5% and did not envisage 'any significant increase in that rate of growth in the early years'.[8] The Government is aiming at an increase of about 5% each year. Taxation, central and local, absorbs over 20% of the total monetary income of the country. The economic survey mission thought it 'hardly possible to envisage any substantial increase in the incidence of taxation'.[9] As regards central government current expenditure, the economic mission took the view that it could be allowed to increase by no more than $4\frac{1}{2}$% per annum between 1960/61 and 1965/66.[10] The Government planned for a somewhat larger rate of increase in recurrent expenditure of about $5\frac{1}{2}$% per annum over the three years 1960/61 to 1963/64. Recently Mr. Kent has made proposals in his report on local government for some increases in local taxation. Possibly more important, he stressed that local authorities could increase their revenue by about one-half (compared with 1961) by collecting all the taxes they were entitled to collect.[11] We understand that failure to enforce the collection of local taxes has been a particular problem in this past year.

The Health Department has been allotted a fairly constant proportion of the current expenditure of the central government since the end of the 1940s. It took about 8% of current expenditure in 1948 : ten years later it was a little over 9%. In 1962/63 it is estimated to be back at around 8%

---

[6] See below.
[7] *Budget Survey 1962/63* p. 17.
[8] *Development Plan for Tanganyika, 1961/62–1963/64*, Dar es Salaam, 1961, p. 8.
[9] The International Bank of Reconstruction and Development, *The Economic Development of Tanganyika*, Dar es Salaam, 1960, p. 1.
[10] *ibid.*, p. 31.
[11] Kent, A. W. *Report on the Services to be Administered by Local Authorities in Tanganyika and the Consequential Financial Arrangements*, 1962.

on current account. Little change in the role of health expenditure in the current budget was envisaged in the three-year development plan.

So far as local revenue is concerned, the health services took 13% of the current expenditure of local government in 1957. By 1961, this had increased slightly to 14%. The new sources of revenue which may be made available to local authorities in the future will all be needed to finance higher expenditure on education. Taking local and central revenue together, in 1961, the health services received about 10% of the total estimated (current and capital) expenditure.[12]

It has been suggested to us that the health services are being allotted an exceptionally low proportion of the budget by international standards. When comparisons are made with countries where income is much higher (such as the United Kingdom) this is certainly the case. But such comparisons are unhelpful. Unfortunately, there is little reliable information on low income countries with which comparisons could be more appropriately made. However, we have examined the statistics in the *Second Report on the World Health Situation*[13] which collects together such information as is available in the reports for various countries. It is not clear though whether the figures in this report refer to central and local government combined, or only to the former. Nor is it possible to ascertain whether they include expenditures by autonomous health agencies and social security systems.

Despite these and other difficulties it would, however, seem that an allocation of 8% of the central budget (or 10% of central and local expenditure combined) is not exceptionally low by international standards. There is, though, a further complicating factor which has to be considered. We have seen from earlier chapters the important part played by the voluntary agencies in the health services in Tanganyika. They are spending, as far as we can calculate,

---

[12] See Chapter I.
[13] World Health Organization, *Second Report on the World Health Situation 1957/1960* Part II, Geneva, 1962.

about one-third of what the central government is spending. In terms of hospital beds, the voluntary agencies certainly play a much larger role in Tanganyika than in Kenya or Uganda, and we doubt whether they are as important in these terms in most of the countries listed in the *Second Report on the World Health Situation*. Additionally, account has to be taken of expenditures incurred by employers. If the expenditures of the voluntary agencies, local authorities and employers were carried by the central government, something like 13% of the central government budget today would be required to finance all the services.

In the light of these facts and comparative estimates for other countries what assumptions should we make concerning the future pattern of expenditure on health services in Tanganyika? If we may judge by the past attitudes of the elected Legislature, by the short-term policy objectives of the government, and by the discussions we had with Ministers, members of the Legislature and officials, we do not think that the health services are likely to receive a substantially higher share of the budget in the longer term than in the short term. The transfer of political power to an elected government has led to a considerable increase in expenditure on education and on economic development. These are clearly the major priorities of the present government and we doubt whether any different view will be taken as far as can be seen ahead. The changing pattern of expenditures on education has been particularly remarkable. In 1948, education took about 6% of the current budget: ten years later it took 17%.

For the purposes of our long-term recommendations we assume, therefore, that current expenditure on health services by central government, local government and voluntary agencies combined will increase by about 4% per annum so that about twice as much will be available in 1980 as in 1962. In selecting this figure we have taken an optimistic view about the expansion of the national income. We anticipate that the enthusiasm and sense of national unity engendered by independence will continue to be harnessed to the task of national development and that this will lead to a somewhat higher rate of growth than in the past. Again, for the purpose of our Report, we take it that broadly the same proportion will continue to be absorbed by taxation.

In deciding to assume a doubling by 1980 in current expenditure on the health services we have taken into account the demands which will be made on the government to improve the services and especially those—like the hospitals—which are predominantly curative rather than preventive. But we do not imagine that the pressures will be nearly as great as those which will develop for an improvement in the education services at every level.

We propose in Chapter 7 the introduction of modest charges for certain health services. We do not, however, regard these as a source of revenue which can materially affect the scale of operation of the services. Also we discuss in Chapter 7 the gradual introduction of a scheme of health insurance. Such a scheme will require additional expenditure, but could well bring in considerable revenue. For the present, however, we do not take account of this possibility in our future estimates.

In total, we assume that in 1980 approximately £7 million (at 1962 prices) will be available for current expenditure on the health services by central government, local government and voluntary agencies combined. Also it is assumed that a sum approaching £1 million will be available on capital account in that year. The rest of this Report is thus concerned with how these sums may be deployed to yield the maximum benefit. For the intervening period we see the health services being developed in stages. We discuss this development, and the steady growth of the plans we put forward for the next twenty years, in our final chapter. Much will depend at every stage on the size and age distribution of the population. We turn now to discuss this question.

At first sight Tanganyika does not appear to have a population 'problem' at all. Despite the abolition of local wars the size of the population changed little over the first few decades of this century and from 1931 to 1948 the rate of growth appears to have been only about 1% per annum. Between 1948 and 1957 the population increased by $1\frac{3}{4}\%$ per annum. Since 1957 no information is available. It is, however, likely that the rate of population increase is now substantially larger than was recorded between 1948 and 1957.

The relatively slow rate of increase is attributable to the high death rate among the African population. Life expectancy at birth was between thirty-five and forty years at the time of the 1957 census. The crude birth rate was some forty-seven per thousand and the infant mortality rate was about 190 per thousand live births—both very high rates by international standards. There were about 5·7 live births per woman. These figures conceal considerable regional variations. While the total fertility rate was six or over in the Lake and Northern Regions it was under five in the Western province. The crude death rate was estimated to be twenty-seven in the Western province and nineteen in the Northern province. Thus, the rate of natural increase also showed wide variations from twenty-seven per thousand in Central Province and twenty-five per thousand in both Lake and Northern provinces to eighteen per thousand in Eastern, Tanga and Western provinces.

At the end of the *Census Report on the African Population (1957)*[14] Dr. Blacker calculated a projection of the population on the assumption of negligible net migration, constant fertility rates and declining mortality rates. On the suggestion of the Population Branch of the United Nations Department of Economic and Social Affairs, he assumed reductions in mortality which would result in an annual gain of 0·5 years in the expectation of life at birth. This implies that the expectation of life will increase from between thirty-five to forty years in 1957 to between fifty-five and sixty years by the year 2000. 'In other words, by the end of this century the level of mortality of Tanganyika's African population will have fallen to that estimated for the Asian population (of Tanganyika) in 1957 or to that calculated for the population of Jamaica in 1950/52 and of Ceylon in 1955.' These rates of declining mortality lead to an increase in the population of 2% per annum for the decade 1961-70, $2\cdot3\%$

14 To be published.

per annum for the decade 1971-80, 2·6 per annum for the decade 1981-90 and 2·8% per annum for the decade 1991 to 2000. On this basis the African population of Tanganyika would increase as in Table I.

Table I

Projected Increase in the African Population of Tanganyika—(1960/2000)

	Thousands
1931	5,023*
1948	7,410*
1960	9,099
1970	11,092
1980	13,924
1990	17,998
2000	23,724
*Census figures.	

In making these calculations Dr. Blacker in no way implied that this was his best estimate of future trends. And there are reasons for believing that the projection under-estimates the likely rate of increase. More rapid declines in mortality could result from the proposals we shall be making later in this Report. We must also consider the strong possibility of an increase in the birth rate. In allowing for this possibility we are given some support by Dr. Blacker who suggests that 'a rise in fertility would seem to be a more plausible prediction than a decline'. The reason he gives for this view is that 'one woman in six reaches her menopause without having borne a child alive. Such an incidence of childlessness indicates a fairly high degree of physiological sterility which an extension of medical services and the eradi-cation of fertility-inhibiting diseases such as malaria may well serve to reduce.'

An increase in the fertility rate may have already occurred since 1957. Some five and a half births per completed family is by no means a high average figure by African standards. The average real income per head in Tanganyika may have increased somewhat since 1957 though whether this has affected standards of living—and especially nutritional standards—in the rural areas is by no means certain. What is certain, however, is that the number of mothers in contact with the maternity services has increased greatly. In 1957 the maternity and child welfare services were in touch with about 5% of mothers, and midwives delivered about 5% of all births. Now in 1961 the maternity and child welfare services are estimated to be in contact at least once with over 40% of all mothers, and midwives delivered 16% of all births (see Chapter 2). In such a short period of time these are, indeed, remarkable changes. It is therefore quite possible that they would have contributed to a decline in miscarriages and still-births and affected the infant mortality rate—estimated in 1957 to be about 190 per thousand.

In later sections of our Report we recommend ways and means by which the maternity and child welfare service may be expanded to reach the vast majority of families. We also propose changes in the training programmes of rural health workers and improvements in organization and supervision which will, we hope, make these services more effective. In all this we stress heavily the part played by these services in promoting better diets, methods of food preparation, child rearing practices and other elements in home economics.[15] The gradual raising of standards in these spheres of family life, together with improvements in the nutrition of pregnant and lactating women and of children in the post-weaning period, could reduce existing death rates quite drastically. Moreover, as venereal disease is brought under control birth rates could rise significantly. This has already

---

[15] For illustrations and analysis of training programmes see Spens, Teresa, *Report on Home Economics in Africa with Special Reference to Rural Areas*, Food and Agricultural Organization, Rome, 1962.

been demonstrated in Southern Sudan by the World Health Organization.[16]

The general spread of the formal education system—to which the government is giving high priority—and the many activities at village level of the self-help and community development movement will all help to foster a healthier way of living. By instruction and example the younger generation of Tanganyikan citizens will learn some knowledge of the laws of health; they will be introduced also to a social climate which will encourage them more readily to accept change. Meanwhile, the integration of development programmes, which will combine the skills of technical departments with the leadership of community development, will be promoting new agricultural techniques and new and better crops in the struggle against the inadequate and ill-balanced diet of the population. All these activities will help in the battle against disease and promote the trend towards population expansion.

It would clearly be absurd to devote so many pages to an account of our ambitious plans to improve health and prolong life, and not also express some confidence in their success. Much too little is, of course, known about the effects of better nutrition, the improved care of children, and the prevention or the eradication of disease on birth and death rates to make it possible to produce in any sense precise predictions of the rate of population growth. We do not anticipate (unless there are major new technological developments) that malaria can be eradicated by 1980—or sleeping sickness, bilharzia or venereal disease—but we hope that their incidence will be greatly reduced. Already Kenya is believed to have an inter-censal rate of growth of about $2\frac{1}{4}\%$ and Uganda of $2\frac{1}{2}\%$.[17] Estimates of the population of the Federation of Rhodesia and Nyasaland for the past ten years, though less certain, show an increase of over $2\frac{3}{4}\%$.[18]

---

[16] Food and Agriculture Organization, *FAO Africa Survey* Report on the possibilities of African rural development in relation to economic and social growth, Rome 1962, p. 15.

[17] Blacker, J. G. C., 'The Demography of East Africa', *The Natural Resources of East Africa*, edited by E. W. Russell, Nairobi, 1962, p. 35.

[18] United Nations, Department of Economic and Social Affairs, *Demographic Yearbook 1960*, New York, 1960.

In view of this experience in African countries to the north, the west and the south, and taking account of the more theoretical arguments we have already adduced, it is possible that the rate of population increase in Tanganyika would be larger than that shown by Dr. Blacker's projection : it might already be exceeding 2% and reach 3% before 1980. Reports on population from the United Nations support this expectation and suggest that the countries of middle Africa may be entering a stage of population explosion.[19] In putting forward this view, we imply no criticism of Dr. Blacker's valuable work on the census report, without which the second half of this chapter could not have been written. For the estimates of cost and health service needs made later in this Report we have accordingly assumed that the population of the country will be about fifteen million in 1980.

We cannot regard the prospect of such a large and rapid increase without concern. In saying this we take full account of the gains in both the length and quality of life which may well accrue from reductions in disease and mortality. It is, indeed, clear that with a smaller burden of disease, more goods and services could be produced. Whether they *will* be produced will depend upon employment opportunities and the stimulus for greater effort. We are aware also that by Asian and European standards the country is sparsely populated : there are no insuperable technical obstacles to growing more food to support a much larger population. Our fears of a growing population are not based upon the classical Malthusian argument of a shortage of food. What does concern us are the limitations and restrictions on the rate of economic and social development which a rapid rate of population growth would inevitably impose. Land and traditional skills are not the only factors of production. If Tanganyika is to make substantial economic progress it needs investment in agriculture, water supplies, industry, transport, communications and in many other fields which make up the infrastructure of development. It needs investment in buildings for the provision of education

---

[19] See, for example, United Nations Department of Economic and Social Affairs, *The Future Growth of World Population*, New York, 1958.

and for the administration of the agencies of development. Whether these expenditures are incurred individually or collectively, publicly or privately, they must fall ultimately on those of working age. And the more children they have to support, the less can the working population make payments towards the development process—whether it is in the form of personal taxes, indirect taxes, educational fees or private savings.

It has been estimated that an under-developed country with its population increasing at $2\frac{1}{2}\%$ per annum must invest from 5 to $12\frac{1}{2}\%$ of the national income in order to keep a constant average amount of working equipment or infrastructure per worker.[20] It is not easy for any relatively poor country to save such a large proportion of its income for investment. It is much harder still where the aim is to reach higher living standards, because such rapidly growing populations must save and invest still more.

If parents had fewer children to support they could help in financing a more ambitious development programme. They could also more easily pay fees to help with the cost of educating a small family than a large one. Many children are at present born, particularly in the rural areas, who have little prospect of attaining full physical and mental development. It is for the people of Tanganyika to say whether they would prefer to have fewer and stronger children than larger numbers of undersized and sickly children.

These are questions which parents must decide. They cannot be the subject of legislation or any form of regulation. The final determinant of family size will be the attitudes of the parents themselves, and these attitudes will be influenced by the values they hold. We believe that the time has come to start providing the knowledge—and the means for those who so desire—by which parents can voluntarily choose the size of their families.

We appreciate that as an expatriate mission our motives for making recommendations in this field could be mis-

---

[20] United Nations, Department of Economic and Social Affairs, *Population Growth and the Standard of Living in Under-Developed Countries*, New York, 1954.

understood or misinterpreted by those who feel strongly about this question. It may be said unkindly that we, as Europeans, have an interest in restricting the number of Africans. A moment's consideration will indicate the absurdity of any such argument. The time is past when power or influence depended on mere numbers; authority and leadership in the world today depend much more on economic power and on the skills and training of a people than on any other factors. And we are arguing for a reduction in births to enable Tanganyika to make a more rapid advance along the road to higher standards of living. The right to make this choice is one of the essential freedoms which newly independent countries can give to their people.

We do not imagine that a campaign to limit births will be either acceptable or practicable in every part of Tanganyika. Progress in this matter as in others will inevitably be uneven. The first step in a policy of birth control is to convince the people that control is possible. And the time has come when this knowledge should be spread all over the country. It would not seem any harder to teach that life can be prevented than that life can be preserved—that the process of human reproduction can be altered either way by human action. This we call the prelimitation phase in slowing down the rate of population growth.

The second phase must be handled with caution and also with insight into the needs and attitudes of different groups of the population. Attempts to persuade parents to limit their families can easily have the reverse effect of stiffening existing patterns of behaviour. Usually the willingness to restrict births depends upon confidence that children who are already born will survive and upon confidence that provision will be made by one means or another for periods of illness, disability and old age. It has to be shown that excessively large families are an economic burden. Yet it is not easy to promote education in favour of limitation when there are traditional economic motives for unlimited fertility. Attitudes are not, however, always built on economic foundations and the careful investigation of social systems will be needed to ascertain those beliefs and values which may conflict with the promotion of family planning. Such studies should start now as part of the prelimitation phase. But where communities or individuals are asking for the means to limit their families, this need should be met. Parents should have the right to choose.

The effort which should be devoted to educational activities in this field depends on the urgency of the population problem. It may be more or it may be less urgent than we have indicated in this chapter.

Virtually no national information on population trends is available which is not five years old. The census is taken no more frequently in East Africa than seemed appropriate in Europe or America over a century ago. This is a matter which deserves much more frequent study. It could be of crucial importance to the whole development plan of the country. We therefore recommend that the Statistical Office should be asked to ascertain trends in fertility and mortality rates at least every five years (on a sample basis if appropriate).

We see the case for family limitation as an integral part of our Report. In Chapter 5 we shall be proposing the wide extension of the maternity and child welfare services within a framework of new health centres and reorganized dispensaries. We would hesitate to give such priority to these services if we did not see them as the precursor to a plan for family limitation—indeed as a bridge along which a limitation programme could later be launched. Progress from bad health to good health inevitably involves progress from high death rates to low death rates. The problem is to prevent the resultant growth in population from transforming economic growth into economic decline. In Europe the decline in birth rates followed many decades after the decline in death rates. It is the objective of modern social and economic planning to reduce this interval of time as far as is possible.

Some readers may sense a contradiction underlying this chapter. In the first part we accepted the fact that the additional expenditure on health services would not be large in the coming years. In the second part we suggested that a plan which makes modest demands on financial resources might have a major impact on mortality rates. We believe that these positions can be reconciled. For it is our contention that the limited resources at present used for health services are not being deployed to the maximum advantage. Too little is at present being spent on preventive services; by a gradual reallocation of the balance of effort between curative and preventive work, dramatic results could be attained. This is one of the principal themes of our Report. Its practical implications are worked out in the chapters which follow.

5 The Strategy of Development: Local Services for Health Care

In the previous chapter we set the probable limits to the health budget for the next twenty years within the context of population growth. The problem of priorities within the broad field of health is the next logical question. The more limited the total resources available, the greater the need to husband those resources carefully; to order priorities in the right balance, and to set clear objectives for the future.

We have assumed that current expenditure on the health services (as defined in earlier chapters) would be allowed to double by 1980. At first sight this may seem a rapid rate of expansion, though it is much slower than was planned at the end of the Second World War. If allowance is made for a 50% increase in population, however, the assumed additional expenditure represents a rise from only about seven shillings per head to less than ten shillings per head. We do not put this figure forward as either a target or a maximum; ambitious goals are needed as well as practical plans. A faster rate of output of trained health workers and the engagement of more foreign doctors could, for example, enable some of our proposals to be implemented by 1975 or even earlier. Similarly, and even more effectively, a slowing down in the rate of population growth could mean the earlier provision of better health services for the whole of the country. If we assume—as we have—a relatively modest rate of growth, it is partly because we do not want our plans to suffer the fate that has befallen all other health plans during the past thirty years, and partly because we

99

have accorded priority to spending on education and agricultural and economic development.

The vast majority of the population live—and will continue to live—in small rural settlements and communities. These are the people of Tanganyika. That is why, in considering the future development of the health services, we begin with the local services on which this rural population so largely depends. For this reason also, it is well to stress at the outset the importance of what the people themselves can do, individually and through collective programmes of self-help and community development, towards the improvement of health at the level of the local community. The standards of health achieved in Tanganyika by 1980 will not be decided by the hospital and the doctor alone. We discuss later the ways in which these movements towards self-improvement can be harnessed to a developing health programme.

We have already traced the evolution of the health services and attempted to describe the present stage of development as we found it in 1961 and 1962. In many respects the record is one of which the country can justifiably be proud, set against the severe limits imposed by economics and population growth. Though we shall draw attention to serious inadequacies in the existing services—especially in the rural areas—we do not wish to belittle in any way the loyal and devoted work of a generation of professional and lay staff in the government services and the voluntary agencies.

Looking back, it is clear that over the past thirty years one of the main deficiencies has been the decreasing role of preventive medicine. With the notable exception of the maternity and child welfare services, the progress of the preventive services has been disappointing. There have undoubtedly been advances in research and useful experiments have been carried out with limited resources, but there have been no significant improvements in the preventive and public health fields over the past decade.

This has not been due to any general disregard of preventive principles. The promotion of preventive services has undoubtedly been in the forefront of the minds of health planners. These good intentions have, however, been the victims of a continuous series of 'temporary' circumstances. Whenever there has been retrenchment, it has been the preventive services which have been cut back. Moreover, the emphasis on curative services has been encouraged by the broad strategy of development laid down thirteen years ago by Dr. Pridie—to expand the curative services so as to demonstrate that trained staff can, within limits, control disease and thus create a climate of opinion in which the public could be persuaded to accept instruction in preventive medicine.

We consider that the time is now past when preventive medicine could be made acceptable only by further expansion of the curative services. The people of Tanganyika now broadly accept the efficacy of Western medicine in its curative aspects. Indeed, there is a danger of too much reliance being placed on the drug and the injection. There is a growing tendency for patients to 'shop around' among various doctors and agencies in the urban areas in the belief that any and every ill will be cured if a powerful enough drug is obtained. All this is understandable, but the lesson which has now to be taught is that there are diseases and many causes of ill-health in Tanganyika for which there is no immediate cure but which may be prevented.

The correction of the present imbalance between the preventive and curative approaches to medicine does not require the creation of a separate 'preventive' branch of the health services. On the contrary, the traditional division between curative measures which benefited the individual and preventive measures which protected the community as a whole is becoming less distinct, if not obsolete. The practical requirements of a pre-eradication malaria programme make it even more so. Although in this Report we distinguish, for administrative purposes, 'personal services' (the subject of this chapter and the next) from 'environmental services' (Chapter 8), we include in personal services all those services which are directed towards the individual—immunization, treatment, the search for infective cases, health education and advice on a personal basis, and periodical health examinations—whether intended mainly for the benefit of the individual or the protection of the community. The association of curative and preventive measures within one integrated local service of personal health care is in line with the philosophy underlying modern medical education. It must be applied in Tanganyika if the harmful effects of excessive (and expensive) specialization are to be avoided, and if popular attitudes to health and disease are to be more firmly rooted in the lessons of nutrition and preventive measures in general.

The responsibility for health education in a broad sense must be shared between a variety of agents. Where people are already working closely together in community development activities, these groups may be the most effective channel of education. Within the organized health services we believe that the health centres of the future should lead the way in the field of health education. We therefore endorse the principle of health centre organization advocated by Dr. Pridie : the creation of a chain of centres which will bring together curative and preventive services. Besides taking their place among the channels of health education, they have a critical part to play as permanent bases from which campaigns can be launched against endemic and epidemic diseases. We are convinced that preventive campaigns must operate through an effective chain of permanent local services which have a continuing responsibility for the treatment of reported cases, the tracing of contacts and follow-up work.

The importance of this approach is now acknowledged even in the case of malaria eradication programmes. The World Health Organization has recently revised its programme for malaria on the basis of experience gained in many countries where it has been found that eradication programmes were much less effective without an adequate 'infrastructure' of the health services—particularly in the later stages. It has, therefore, withdrawn its offer of immediate technical aid to eradication programmes in countries where the infrastructure is inadequate, and substituted offers of aid towards a 'Pre-eradication Programme'. This means, in short, the creation of a rural health service from which eradication campaigns can later be mounted. Our recommendations as they relate to the rural services are intended to fulfil all the requirements of a Pre-eradication Programme, thus making it possible for Tanganyika to apply for technical and material aid from WHO for the attack on malaria.

It is this reasoning which leads us to advocate the re-organization of the whole of the dispensary service which is curative in a first-aid sense in its outlook, and to recommend considerable changes in the approach to the training of those who at present staff the local services. In effect, we take still further and apply the principles which have been expressed in previous health plans. While our specific proposals do not differ greatly in structural form from what has been proposed before, they do involve radical changes in the way in which the local services are actually operated.

Perhaps the main impression we have gained from our survey is the great variation that at present exists in the standards, efficacy and scope of the local services. In some parts of the country the most usual place to go for initial diagnosis and for simple treatments is a hospital out-patient department. In the towns, the hospital would typically be a government one and treatment would be free; in the rural areas the hospital would typically be owned by a voluntary agency and there would often be charges to pay. In other parts of the country there are a few health centres where a team of health workers is available to provide free services. Over most of the country the first place to go to get medical attention is a dispensary—a term which is applied to a wide variety of different units. There is the central government dispensary which is free, typically has some twenty beds, and is under the direction of a medical assistant. There is the local authority dispensary where charges may or may not be levied and which may be staffed by a rural medical aid or by a tribal dresser—often isolated, ill-educated and ill-supplied. Finally, there is the voluntary agency dispensary which will usually levy charges and may be under the direction of trained staff, untrained staff, visiting staff or no 'staff' at all. Thus, initial consultations may be free or subject to a variety of charging systems. They may be conducted by doctors, medical assistants, medical aids, dressers, sisters, nurses, nuns, priests, or by lay missioners, wives and families. Partly because of this wide variation in facilities and standards, patients in some areas search for *the* injection or *the* drug which will perform the 'miracle' expected of Western medical care.

One reason for including in this Report a long historical chapter was to explain the evolution of the present initial consultation arrangements. For only by understanding their historical antecedents can one explain such a confusion of medical aid. The past has left Tanganyika with the products of many different courses of training and many different systems of apprenticeship—some now abandoned, some down-graded, others up-graded. The country is littered, like Africa itself, with many monuments to the expansionist ambitions and the humanitarian ideals of a variety of agencies—old missionary dispensaries now derelict for lack of staff, new self-help dispensaries hopefully awaiting their first incumbent, new voluntary agency dispensaries marking out fresh outposts. In the midst of these thousand odd first-aid and curative units can be found a few demonstrations of the new philosophy of integrated health care—the twenty-two health centres representing no more than a token of a plan adopted in principle thirteen years ago.

Since the development of the local authority dispensary services, the numerical expansion of units has always proceeded much faster than the number of persons adequately trained to staff them. As a result, the few trained staff who are available have always had to undertake too wide a range of duties to be able to perform all of them effectively. By expanding and improving training programmes it will gradually be possible to separate and designate more clearly the responsibilities of skilled staff at different levels. This is one need; an equally important one is greatly to extend the supervisory and educational functions of the more highly trained staff.

Local Services for Health Care

The evidence we have received and the observations which we ourselves have been able to make have convinced us that such is the strain on these categories of staff that the task of supervising outlying health centres and dispensaries is inadequately performed at present. Certain minimum supervisory functions of an administrative nature have to be performed, such as the inspection of records and the distribution of pay. While these tasks have to be carried out it has been the professional aspects of supervision and instruction which have been curtailed or wholly omitted. It is unreasonable to expect staff with the limited training of the rural medical aid or the tribal dresser to remain enthusiastic and efficient while working at isolated posts, unless the standard of their work is regularly reviewed, and they are given further and continuing education from a medical practitioner.

The number of medical practitioners at work in the rural areas employed by government and voluntary agencies combined is far too small to provide an adequate service in any respect. Moreover, too many tasks at present fall upon any doctor who is available. He is not only expected to supervise the outlying health services but he has to exercise responsibility for environmental hygiene over the whole area. He has to undertake medico-legal work in cases ranging from drunkenness to insanity and homicide: this can cause absence from his base for days on end. He has to take part in the clinical work of the hospital itself where he and the other members of the hospital staff are subjected to an impossible variety of different demands. They are expected to divide their time between long queues of unselected out-patients arriving at every hour of the day and night, and heterogeneous collections of in-patients who overfill the beds or overflow on to the floor between them. They are also expected to give special attention to Grade I patients. In addition, there falls on the staff of the government hospital the full brunt of certification duties—army recruits, employees, prisoners and tax defaulters. The result of all this is to prevent the hospitals from performing their proper functions in a rational system of medical care, and to prevent any adequate supervision of satellite health centres and dispensaries.

The interests of the efficient working of the hospital require that patients who can more appropriately as well as more cheaply be looked after elsewhere should be diverted to separately organized local services. The interests of efficiency also require that patients who really need the special facilities of the hospital should more frequently be able to reach them. The hospital should be used as a hospital and not be swamped by every conceivable kind of demand for medical attention. At present, it is difficult for patients who really need hospital care to find their way to hospitals from the more remote parts of the country; this may be because roads are impassable at times or because the journey would be too much for the patient. But it is also often because the means of transport are not made available or because harassed hospital staffs have to discourage referrals to a hospital which is already more than full.

A plan for rationalization, therefore, must involve a re-distribution and a better ordering of patient care functions between hospitals and other health facilities. The key to any such plan is an improvement in the services outside the hospital. In more developed countries there might be available outside the hospital the services of the family doctor, the factory doctor, the school doctor, the police doctor, the prison doctor and many medico-social workers, all of whom would be undertaking functions which are at present expected of most hospitals in Tanganyika. It is not possible to envisage such a large number of different agencies and specialized services in a country as poor as Tanganyika. However, where any of these services is available, or can be usefully developed within an overall plan, this should be encouraged, both for the sake of the hospital and the local health centre. But there must be in each community or settlement area at least one type of service which is staffed by a medical practitioner who is not based on a hospital.

These are the main reasons for reorganizing and improving the local personal health services: to give to the rural population a better medical service; to infuse into these local services a preventive approach; to provide a continuous system of supervision of the staff and health education of the public; to link closely the work of these services and the movement for self-help and community development, and to protect the hospitals and so enable them to perform their special and particular functions.

Accordingly, we recommend that the dispensary system be entirely recast. While there are some good dispensaries, the standards of building, equipment, staff and supplies of many of them are lamentable. We propose, therefore, a wholly new system of supervision and a radically different system of staffing so that dispensaries become participants in preventive as well as in curative work. They will, under our recommendations, be wholly staffed by trained auxiliary grades even if this means the temporary closure of some peripheral units or their down-grading to first-aid posts. This change in the function of dispensaries should be marked by calling them 'health clinics'. These health clinics would refer selected cases to health centres which would be responsible for providing supervision, training and leadership for all their satellite clinics, as well as a high standard of clinical care for referred cases.

At the next level we envisage a series of health centres referring cases to an improved and enlarged area hospital. There should, however, be a separate medical and nursing area team acting in close liaison with the hospital and the environmental health service which has the responsibility of leading and supervising all the health units in the area— the centres with their satellite clinics.[1] The essence of the system is the maintenance of a high standard of supervision and 'postgraduate education' at every level. Each health centre must be an example to its clinics. Each parent hospital must be an example of good medical care and must support its surrounding health centres in a variety of ways. The success of the whole system will, of course, depend on the training and morale of all the staff. Though our discussion of new training programmes comes towards the end of this Report (Chapter 9) it is the lynch pin of the whole plan.

[1] See Organizational Chart Appendix A.

Here we stress the importance of a health education approach and the need to focus the training of the Tanganyikan medical practitioner on his role as the leader of the health centre team.

These recommendations are intended to apply as much to the towns and urban areas as to the rural areas. This is essential if the hospitals are to gain the protection which they need to develop their proper role in the health services. Thus, there should be one or more health clinics situated in the residential areas of the towns and on the roads of access from the country. Towards the middle of the town there should be a health centre, performing for the town health clinics the same function as the rural health centres perform for village health clinics. This town health centre could act as the headquarters for the area medical officer and his team who will be responsible for supervising all the local personal health and environmental services in the area. In those towns which also have a hospital, the health centre might well be sited nearby but on no account should it be under its control. The health centre may need to be kept open until after dark, to prevent improper demands being made on the hospital casualty department.

In considering the number and distribution of health centres and hospitals needed to provide an acceptable minimum standard of service, we have had regard to our terms of reference which require us to examine the question of 'even coverage' for the whole country. We take this to mean a reasonable balance between the needs of town and country and between country areas with varying population densities. The main problem here, however, is the great variation in population densities throughout the country as a whole. If medical facilities were sited according to strict population ratios, they would be geographically inaccessible to large numbers of people. If the facilities were distributed evenly many health clinics would have few people to serve. We have therefore tried to strike a balance between the various factors so that as few people as possible will be deprived of access to health services by the physical difficulties of reaching or being reached by them.

Local Services for Health Care

After a careful study of the facts of population and land, and after making allowance for the possibility of a population of fifteen million in 1980, we have reached the conclusion that the country can be provided with an acceptable minimum standard if it is served by forty health areas, each with an average of five health centres and twenty-five health clinics. Under such a plan, and assuming no substantial change in the pattern of population distribution, most people would have a branch of the health services within walking distance. In the more remote parts of the country one hospital will be sufficient for two areas. Thus, we envisage twenty-two areas sharing eleven hospitals, and the remaining eighteen areas each having exclusive use of a hospital. We shall be suggesting in the next chapter that three of these twenty-nine hospitals should be equipped to act as reference hospitals for neighbouring area hospitals.

This plan is based on the assumption that each 'unit' (the health centre with its five clinics) will broadly be serving about 50,000 people in sparsely populated areas and up to 100,000 people in densely populated areas. This is the plan which we have developed in detail for costing purposes.[2] Obviously after a more detailed study of the facts, the plan will have to be modified in some areas, such as where major development is occurring or where the population is mainly nomadic.

The work of each health 'unit' should be organized so as to improve the health of all the people living within its catchment area. One responsibility of the unit, but by no means the most important, will be to diagnose and treat the simpler maladies and refer the more difficult cases to the hospital. A second responsibility will be educational—to teach the local population to provide better care for sick persons in their own homes, to adopt a more balanced diet and understand its significance for health, to see the importance of nutritious foods and the special needs of infants, children and pregnant and lactating women, to appreciate the need for cleanliness in the handling of food and the simple lessons of infection and, in general, to persuade the people by demonstration as well as by word of mouth to accept

[2] See Appendix B.

healthier modes of living. These activities need to be undertaken in close conjunction with the local agents of the environmental health, agricultural and veterinary services, with the local schools, and with the local community development committees and officials. Thirdly, the staff of the health unit should know the habits of the local people and observe and report any significant changes in the pattern of disease. Thus, the eyes and ears of all the staff working in the unit should be directed at the local community: they should know all their people—not just those who live near the services or attend frequently, but those who live further away. From the start, the staff should attempt to carry advice, treatment and supervision into the home.

The *health clinic* should perform the simpler curative and preventive tasks. In particular, it should concentrate on providing standardized specific treatments for acute infections and detecting malnutrition (particularly in children) in its early stages. It should, however, also cater for the minor ailments and injuries of daily life, partly because this is a natural and proper expectation of the people, and partly to protect the health centre from being overwhelmed by this type of need. The clinic should also concentrate on maternity work: ante-natal services should be maintained with the initial aim to provide one consultation for each mother at about the fifth or sixth month of pregnancy. But the emphasis in all maternity work should not be on the delivery itself (unless an abnormal birth is expected) but on using the event of birth as a way of introducing the elements of infant and child care. The examination of children should be frequent during the period of weaning: regular, but less frequent, examinations of children should be made up to the age of puberty. Such work should be undertaken in close association with the schools. These should be the main functions of a health clinic. It should, however, also take part in immunization and health education campaigns planned and organized from its parent health centre.

The initial staff of a health clinic should consist of one

medical aid[3] (who would be in charge), one trained maternity aid,[4] one nursing orderly, and two subordinate staff. Existing tribal dressers will be eligible for appointment as nursing orderlies. Later, it may be necessary to provide a second maternity aid if there is a demand for more services. The clinic building should be maintained at a high standard of hygiene as an example to the local community. Supplies of drugs used in the treatment of acute infections should be adequately stocked. This is seldom the case at present.

Though a *health centre* should provide all the services of a health clinic to its immediate district, its principal function is to provide continuous education and supervision for the staff of its five health clinics (including the staff of the clinic which is incorporated in the centre itself). The director of the centre should be a Tanganyika-trained practitioner[5] who must set and maintain standards throughout his whole health unit. Accompanied by his staff nurse, he must spend as much time outside his centre as inside—undertaking regular visits to each clinic at least once a fortnight. These routine visits should not only be used for administrative purposes and for planning immunization and health education campaigns (though these tasks are essential); they should primarily be used for teaching purposes. The medical practitioner should himself undertake part of the regular work of the clinic as well as diagnosing and treating the more difficult cases for which the medical aid wants advice and help. In these ways, he will be able to raise the standard of work of the medical aid.

The staff nurse, in her relations to the work of the maternity aid at the clinic, would have similar functions of teaching and supervision to perform as the medical practitioner. She also has a vital part to play in the field of health education and the care of children.

---

[3] We omit the word 'rural' from the title of this auxiliary as we propose that some health clinics and health centres where they will be working will be sited in and around towns.
[4] A new category with a two-year training comparable and complementary to that of a medical aid—see Chapter 9.
[5] For a discussion of his medical training and functions see later and also Chapter 9.

Attached to each health centre there should be a number of beds for maternity cases. The number and use of such beds will depend mainly on the availability of skilled aid with the management of cases which are considered likely to be difficult. Normally the beds should be used for those requiring observation. Abnormal cases should be sent to the hospital whenever possible.

Also at the health centre there should be a number of 'holding' beds. One use of such beds is to accommodate patients who are awaiting transfer to hospital. A second use is to facilitate medical supervision during more serious illnesses which are, however, expected to be of short duration. The management of such illnesses at the health centre economizes in transport and protects the hospital from treating these short-term cases which can be effectively looked after elsewhere. We envisage about twenty beds at health centres.

The use of 'holding' beds should vary according to local circumstances. In more remote areas they will be appropriately used for a wider range of purposes than in more populated parts of the country. We are well aware that the provision of such beds might lead to some health centre staffs making more use of them than is intended and doing this at the expense of their primary duties. We hope that the training of the Tanganyikan medical practitioner will give him no incentive to convert his health centre into a district hospital.

Apart from his role as medical teacher and as clinician responsible for the more difficult cases referred from health clinics, the director of the health centre should be concerned with the collection of certain health statistics and with studying the prevalence of diseases and their local epidemiology. From his close acquaintance with the area he will be in a position to organize appropriate preventive measures and to co-operate and advise on the local execution of campaigns initiated through the central epidemiological service.[6] He will also work closely with the local government environmental services and local community development agencies

---

[6] See Chapter 10.

as the adviser on all the health needs of the area—individual and collective.

To undertake all these duties successfully, to act as leader, administrator, teacher, adviser and clinician, the director of a health centre will need skill, training and personal qualities of a high order. It is for this reason that we attach so much importance to the system of training. He must be taught to diagnose and treat the common medical ailments including acute mental disorders. He must have an understanding of surgical practice but would not normally be expected to undertake—or have the facilities for—operative surgery, other than minor out-patient and casualty surgery. He must have skill in supervising pregnancy in all its stages, conducting deliveries and dealing with some complications such as those requiring low forceps, episiotomy etc. In all these fields he must be taught to judge the need for consultation and specialist care and be able to continue treatments initiated at or prescribed by the hospital. He must above all have a good basic training in social and preventive medicine, an understanding of nutrition, of health education and methods of communication.[7]

The staff of the health centre will vary according to the number and needs of the population it is serving. For costing purposes we have assumed that an average centre will have the following staff :

One medical practitioner, Director
One senior medical aid, Deputy Director
Two medical aids

(The two medical aids between them will be responsible for laboratory and pharmacy work in the centre and for deputizing for medical aids in outlying clinics during leave and sickness.)

One nurse, Grade A
Two nurses, Grade B
Two maternity aids. (One of whom would spend much of

---

[7] These functions are paraphrased from the World Health Organization Study Group Report, *Internationally Acceptable Minimum Standards of Medical Education,* Technical Report Series No. 239, Geneva, 1962, and elaborated in Chapter 9 and Appendix C.

her time deputizing for maternity aids in outlying clinics during leave and sickness.)

One nursing orderly
One driver
Five subordinate staff (cleaners, laundry workers etc.).

In addition to the above there should be initially attached to the centre a health inspector and/or health orderly for environmental or public health duties in the area. We shall, however, be making proposals in Chapter 8 for the closer integration of the health inspectorate with local government in the rural areas as well as the towns.

Once the basic complement is provided at health centres all over the country, the next stage would be to add another practitioner to the unit so that more time could be devoted to clinical and teaching duties. An additional maternity aid should also be employed in each health clinic until all confinements and infants are in contact with the local health services. When this stage of expansion is reached, the next step would be for the second practitioner to be detached from the health centre and to open a second centre in part of what had previously been the area of the first centre. In this way, health centre functions would gradually be extended to service more people. But this is to look a long way ahead.

The immediate planning problem for the Ministry of Health will be to decide which existing units of the health services should be designated for upgrading to health centres or health clinics. Most of the existing dispensaries are far below the standard which we regard as suitable for health clinics, but some of the central government's bedded dispensaries may prove suitable for adaptation as health centres. In the next chapter we shall suggest that the hospital services should be concentrated on a number of hospitals substantially larger in size than the present average. Thus, some hospital buildings will no longer be needed for their present purposes. A number might prove to be suitable for adaptation as health centres. Many small hospitals and dispensaries are at present owned by voluntary agencies. We leave, however, until Chapter 7 a discussion of the role which we hope the voluntary agencies will play within this plan for the reorganization of the local services.

A *health area* is the term we use to describe the area served by five health centres, with their satellite health clinics, which are under a common supervision and share the use of one common hospital, though in some cases two areas will be using the same hospital. Although the same geographical area may be served by one hospital and supervised by one administrative head, the staff of the hospital and the staff responsible for the non-hospital health services must be kept separate so far as their responsibilities are concerned but not, of course, in terms of co-operative relationships.[8] This is essential if the hospital staff are to give proper attention to the work of the hospital. It is also essential to ensure that in every area the work of supervision and education is effectively undertaken. Many medical practitioners with combined clinical and supervisory responsibilities are under heavy pressure to devote an excessive proportion of their time to the former. This is not the first time that this has been pointed out in a Tanganyikan report.[9] The supervisory staff will need to work in close relationship with the hospital, and may undertake occasional clinical responsibilities at the hospital, but they must not have any major duties which could interfere with the regularity and thoroughness of their supervision of the health units.

We envisage that normally the area supervisory staff will be based on the town health centre. Their functions in relation to health centres will be very similar to those of health centres in relation to health clinics.

To carry out these supervisory functions and to implement the process of referral over the distances involved it is essential to have adequate means of communication and transport. We therefore recommend that where neither telephone nor telegraph facilities exist radio communication should be established between the health centres and the area headquarters and hospital. The additional value of improved communications, for the organization of ambulance services

---

[8] See Organizational Chart, Appendix A.
[9] See Chapter 1.

and specialist medical consultation, is described in Chapter 6 and for administrative purposes in Chapter 10.

The supervisory staff of the health area will also be responsible for the environmental services of the area. These are discussed in Chapter 8.

The supervisory staff of the health area should consist of the following:

One Area Health Officer who would be responsible to the Regional Medical Officer for all health services in the area other than the hospital and any other specialized units located in his area. It is desirable that an Area Officer should have undertaken formal postgraduate training in public health and have operated a health centre himself for some considerable time. In the early stages of development it will not be possible to ensure that all Area Officers have had this experience but in the long run this is essential.

Two medical practitioners to assist the Area Officer and deputize for him in his absence and for health centre practitioners during leave and sickness.

One nurse of sister rank, with postgraduate training designed to enable her to supervise all nursing, maternity and child welfare work.

One nurse, Grade A, to assist the above and deputize for health centre nurses on leave and sickness.

One mental welfare assistant[10] to supervise arrangements for the after-care of mental patients and generally to undertake and supervise social work concerning mental patients.

Two medical aids for relief purposes.

One administrative assistant[10] to take the burden of administrative work off the Area Health Officer.

One clerk, two drivers and four subordinate staff.

These proposals may appear to represent a generous staffing for the primary tasks of supervision. We intend, however, that these responsibilities should be thoroughly performed. For we regard supervision as a continuous educational process for all grades of staff to which the more traditional administrative and disciplinary aspects of supervision should be subservient. We do not envisage simply a

[10] See Chapter 9 for suggested training.

routine series of visits paid by the area staff. There are a variety of different systems of supervision which call for much imagination, experimentation and flexibility. We would like to see the team from area headquarters spending a week in turn with the staff of each health unit—out in the field rather than in a health centre. There is, too, ample scope for experimenting with the uses of simple mobile units for supervisory, educational and demonstration purposes.

The practitioner from area headquarters could relieve the health centre director of his duties while the latter participates in such exercises; the area medical aids could deputize for health unit aids while they attend for further instruction in the field with the area officer and his staff. Activities of this kind could take place for several months in the year with the area team possibly spending three weeks in four out in the field. During other months the area officer might organize intensive public educational campaigns in co-operation with or at the request of local agencies. These campaigns might be directed at particular diseases (e.g. malaria, venereal diseases or tuberculosis) or at particular needs (e.g. latrines, clean food, clean water or family planning). It will be for the area headquarters to stimulate local action in every way possible with 'health weeks', 'nutrition weeks', 'infant feeding weeks', and so forth, supported with film shows, exhibitions, demonstrations, and active participation by all groups and leaders in the community. By leadership and example, area headquarters must work with the people to effect change, and with its own field staff to provide a service of constantly improving quality.

Viewed from national headquarters, the area and unit structure, with supervision at every level and with clinics in every small centre of population, will need to be used to service major campaigns against specific diseases. More intensive campaigns are desperately needed against tuberculosis, venereal diseases, eye diseases and malaria. All such campaigns need a network of closely integrated clinics. They cannot succeed without this basic permanent structure of organized health services. The strategy of health development for the mass of the people thus determines the first priority as the expansion and staffing of the local health units and health area headquarters.

We accept that our initial target of units and staffing for forty health areas is no more than a bare minimum of health service provision. As finance and trained staff become available we would like to see the number of areas substantially increased. The areas with the largest population should certainly be divided into two areas. And in the long run we would like to see more and more of the health clinics converted into full health centres. Our initial target represents, therefore, no more than a minimum base from which major preventive campaigns can be launched with vigour and imagination.

6 The Hospital Services

One reason for recommending the major reorganization of the local health services described in the last chapter was to alter the character of the demands made upon the hospitals. Our recommendations are aimed to keep patients with minor illnesses out of hospital and away from the hospital. Except for obvious emergencies all the patients reaching the general hospitals should first be examined in a health clinic or health centre, or by an outside doctor, and selected as needing more specialized treatment than can be provided at the health centre, the health clinic or at home. For this reason alone changes will be needed in the hospitals as well as the local services if they are to fulfil their proper role in a national health service.

At present the hospital tends to be incorrectly and inefficiently used partly because of the absence of effective alternatives outside it, and partly because there are relatively few families in Tanganyika which have the facilities or knowledge for home nursing and the self treatment of minor ailments and injury. Western medicine is now accepted to an embarrassing extent, but for historical reasons it has only been experienced, by the majority, as an institutional service. The tradition of free attention for government servants at a hospital has led all sections of the population to regard the hospital as the right place to go with any kind of illness or injury.

A general hospital should, in our view, be a place which provides care of a kind which cannot be provided adequately or economically elsewhere. It may be because specialized equipment or accommodation is required. It may be because specialized medical, surgical or nursing skill is required. It is for one or more of these reasons that a patient should be admitted to hospital. In the future we envisage patients being referred to and from the hospital: to the hospital for diagnosis and specialized care, from the hospital for follow-on treatment and observation. The clinics, health centres and hospitals are interdependent in our proposed reforms; each makes the other more effective and also more economical.

The Faults of the Present Hospitals

The reorganization and development of the initial consultation services both in the towns and in the rural areas should protect the hospital from the excessive and growing demands being made upon it. This will in itself make it possible for the hospitals to provide a better service.

But the hospitals do not only need protection: most of them need changes as drastic as those which we have suggested for the services outside. Indeed, the majority of the present hospitals have neither the staff nor the facilities to act as 'hospitals' in the sense in which we use the term. 'Hospitals' which lack adequate sluices and toilet facilities hardly merit that description. And if a hospital is intended to provide a particular type of medical care for the seriously ill, an institution which lacks any resident medical staff should not be classified as such. If a hospital is intended to offer the services of a team of professionally qualified or trained staff supported by adequate facilities it must be of a certain size to justify their employment. But more than half of the 'hospitals' in Tanganyika which have resident medical staff have less than 100 beds: only 7% of hospitals have more than 200 beds.

In saying all this we are saying no more than could be said about many other services in Tanganyika. There is not enough. And what there is could be much better. In saying it about the hospitals, we imply no criticism of those who established them or those who work in them at present. The creation, so to speak, of 'all-purpose' health institutions over much of the country may have made the best use of extremely limited resources in the earliest stages of development, and made such resources available—at least in theory—to a larger proportion of the population. But recent progress in education has now made it possible to plan for a rapid increase in trained staff by 1980. This will make it possible to staff different types of health services in every area, and for 'hospitals' to be transformed from 'all-purpose' institutions into centres of specialized services.

In reviewing the present situation, we are not questioning whether these institutions have performed or are performing a valuable function—that goes without saying—we are asking how many are suited to fulfil the role of a hospital within the system of medical care which we recommend. By this criteria most hospitals in Tanganyika are found wanting.

Most of them are too small and ill-equipped. The dispersed and sometimes haphazard layout of buildings militates against cleanliness and economy. Domestic and subordinate staff are often inadequate in number and training because the hospital does not offer adequate wages. At many voluntary hospitals patients have to rely on food supplied by their families. Apart from the often woeful nature of these meals, the hospital fails to teach the lesson that nutrition and health are connected. Although half of the hospital population consists of children, only the big hospitals have children's wards. Clinical records are inadequate. The staff, medical and auxiliary, are grossly overworked and often demoralized by all-purpose duties and by too frequent posting from one unit to another. Under these conditions it is remarkable how much good medicine and surgery is practised.

Of all these faults the most important are the last two—the shortage and impermanence of qualified staff. And the position is made worse by the assortment of duties which have to be performed by hospital staffs and which we referred to in the last chapter. Not only are professional staff undertaking duties in the hospital which should be undertaken outside; many are having to perform a large part of the administrative and even clerical work of the hospital itself. Much too large a share of these duties falls on the shoulders of medical and nursing staff. Outside the two main hospitals, there are few qualified and experienced clerks in the hospital service. There are no lay administrators.

Our Proposals for General Hospitals

Practitioners referring patients from a health centre expect not just a second opinion but a better opinion and better care than can be provided in a health centre. The hospital must therefore have not just one or two doctors but several, so that they can devote themselves to particular fields of work (particularly surgery and obstetrics) without being necessarily in the academic sense qualified specialists. To assist them in their work, they will need a properly staffed X-ray unit and a properly staffed pathological laboratory. Trained staff in the ancillary departments and several medical practitioners can only be justified economically if they are given enough selected cases to use their specialized skills for most of their time. This means that hospitals must be much larger than is at present typical of Tanganyika. Indeed, we have formed the view that eventually a hospital must have a minimum of 200 beds.

In 1960, the twelve largest general hospitals in Tanganyika were as shown in Table I.

There are only six general hospitals in the whole country which have over 200 beds; of the twelve largest hospitals, five are owned by voluntary agencies. It is therefore of great importance that the voluntary agencies should participate in the plans we put forward. We shall be making proposals in the next chapter which will, we hope, encourage them to do so. By closer integration of the work of all these agencies—aiming, at the same time, at quality and concentration rather than dispersion and duplication—we believe that a better hospital service in fewer hospitals can be attained.

Hospitals of 200-250 beds justify some specialization and some auxiliary departments but they do not justify the employment of the wide range of specialists which are needed to provide every type of patient with care of the highest

Table I

The largest hospitals in Tanganyika in 1960

Beds	Place	Province	Owner
600	Dar es Salaam		Government
410	Tanga	Tanga	Government
263	Moshi	Northern	Government
236	Peramiho	Southern	Benedictine
220	Mwanza	Lake	Government
216	Tabora	Western	Government
193	Sumbe	Lake	White Fathers
190	Ndanda	Southern	Benedictine
186	Bumbuli	Tanga	Lutheran
184	Morogoro	Eastern	Government
178	Ifakara	Eastern	Capuchin
170	Dodoma	Central	Government

quality. Nor do they justify the full range of auxiliary departments which are to be found in large hospitals throughout the world. There is, therefore, a need for a system of grading within the hospital sector as well as within the local services. We recommend, therefore, that there should be two categories of general hospitals which we call 'A' and 'B' to avoid the territorial associations which would be implied if we had used such terms as 'regional', 'provincial' or 'district'. The 'A' hospitals are hospitals with over 500 beds which have specialist staff in the major specialities (including pathology and radiology), train doctors at the postgraduate level and at least one will train undergraduate medical practitioners,[1] train nurses, serve as the local general hospital for their own area and act as a reference hospital for the 'B' hospitals of several other areas. It will not be economic or practicable to staff and equip a hospital (or group hospital) of less than 500 beds for these functions,

---

[1] See Chapter 9.

and it is assumed that Tanganyika can afford only three such hospitals in the foreseeable future. The 'B' hospitals have 200-250 beds and act as the parent hospital for one or more health areas. It is as 'B' hospitals that we hope that some of the existing voluntary institutions (whether listed above or not) will take their place in a reorganized system. 'Hospitals' which are not designated for development as 'B' hospitals will gradually become redundant or be reorganized as health centres or clinics. We shall suggest that grants for voluntary hospitals which are not scheduled for development as 'B' hospitals should be gradually withdrawn. No more small hospitals should be built by government or voluntary agencies.

The category 'B' hospital is intended to set professional standards and to support the health centres and other health services in its area. It must be designed to perform this function as economically and efficiently as possible. It cannot have a large or fully specialized staff but should have the basic laboratory and X-ray facilities to support sound clinical work. (A hypothetical establishment devised for costing purposes is given in Appendix B, Table V.) Its medical staff should include ex-registrars from the Princess Margaret Hospital who have had a good practical training in the major clinical disciplines. They should be given opportunities to return to an 'A' hospital from time to time for further postgraduate experience. And just as the 'A' hospital provides support for all hospital medical officers, so each 'B' hospital in co-operation with the Health Area Headquarters staff, must act as a 'postgraduate' centre for all practitioners in charge of health centres, medical aids and other auxiliaries working in the area. Some of these hospitals should be approved for pre-registration resident posts for Tanganyika-trained practitioners.

It is essential that there should be an adequate number of medical staff and that their whole time should be concentrated on the work for which they have been trained. The recommendations which we made in the last chapter were intended to lighten very considerably the duties of hospital medical officers by the transfer of responsibility for environmental health and the supervision of surrounding health services to separate medical staff,[2] and by the abolition of the ever-open clinic and the transfer of its functions to the health centres. The latter change should greatly reduce the number of patients attending out-patient departments. Apart from emergencies, the only patients seen would be those who are specifically referred or who are attending for 'follow-up' purposes. These will, however, be the more difficult cases requiring on average much more time than needs to be devoted to the typical out-patient who attends at present. Though the hospital will be seeing fewer patients in total than at present, it will be seeing many more *referred* patients.

The change in the role of the hospital will also affect in-patient departments. Minor medicine and surgery will in general be replaced by more major medicine and surgery; normal obstetrics will be increasingly replaced by abnormal obstetrics. The whole tempo of hospital work will change and much greater demands will be made for drugs and equipment and, above all else, for skilled manpower.

A considerable amount of medical and nursing time can be released for the performance of medical and nursing duties by the introduction of trained lay administrators. In the case of 'B' hospitals we suggest that they should be responsible to the senior medical officer. We put forward in Chapter 9 proposals for a system of training for this grade of administrative assistant who would be able to relieve medical and nursing staff of a wide range of administrative and clerical duties.

Despite these reliefs a 'B' hospital will still need several medical practitioners. Their training will qualify the new Tanganyika-trained practitioners for hospital posts as assistants to specialists and for responsible work of a general nature, and we hope that some of them will be given opportunities of this kind. But the majority of these practitioners *must* be recruited for work in the health centres. The new training programme recommended in Chapter 9 cannot,

---

[2] See Organizational Chart, Appendix A.

therefore, be expected to make much of a direct contribution to hospital staffing for many years to come.

If the fullest value is to be obtained from the services of the relatively few doctors who will be available for the hospitals, auxiliaries will still need to be employed to assist them and deputize for them. Hitherto medical assistants have filled this role, but the recruitment of medical assistants is to cease, because it is expected that few young men will be leaving school in the future at Standard X. In future, these auxiliaries will have to be found from some other source, and the only possibility is to select suitable medical aids for further training. Posts in the hospitals will deserve grading as Senior Medical Aid positions. Medical assistants have, however, been undertaking work which would normally be done by qualified doctors if they were available and it is unlikely that many medical aids, even with further training, will be able to undertake work of this responsibility. The conclusion is inescapable. A larger proportion of the medical work in hospitals will have to be undertaken by qualified medical practitioners. This prospect makes it all the more necessary to ensure the employment of all professional staff for the purposes for which they were trained. It also reinforces the argument for concentrating hospital work of a proper standard in a smaller number of hospitals of larger average size.

To make the most economical use of skilled staff, the principle of 'progressive patient care'[3] used in America and other western countries should be introduced in Tanganyika. The application of the principle in these 'B' hospitals will differ in detail, but the principle is if anything more applicable. There is everything to be said for concentrating rare skills and equipment and expensive procedures in one part of the hospital where patients are cared for during the most critical phases of their medical or surgical treatment. From the patients' point of view, progress from this 'intensive care unit' by stages to the 'self care unit' where help from attendant relatives can be encouraged should present no difficulty at all in Africa. It would rather be an instance of

---

[3] Porter, K. R. D. 'Ward Design', *Lancet*, 1962, **2**, 35.

western medicine conforming, belatedly, to indigenous attitudes and rationalizing them. The system is compatible with graded accommodation for amenity patients providing it is accepted that there is no place (or need) for grades in the intensive care units. The layout of existing hospitals will present difficulties, but where major alterations are to be undertaken or a new hospital is to be built the 'progressive patient care' principle should be introduced.

The principle of a central sterile supply service, which has already been introduced at the Princess Margaret Hospital, should be applied elsewhere if practicable. Bacteriological control is a limiting factor but a study of how far the system can be adapted profitably for partial application in smaller hospitals should be worthwhile. The economics of the use of disposable equipment should also repay study. In every respect, the area hospital should set a standard of hygiene and cleanliness for the neighbourhood. Much dinginess and dirt in hospitals arises out of the traditional (British colonial) open pavilion layout, as constant foot traffic carries dust and mud into wards and clinics and it is not long before it is transferred from floor to linen. Here again good design can bring down cleaning costs—fewer entrances, covered ways, no through-ward traffic, more baths.

The 'B' hospital will also act as the ambulance station for its area or areas. Each health centre should be provided with one vehicle but its primary purpose is to transport health centre staff on their tours of supervision, instruction and inspection. In extreme emergency this vehicle may be used to convey a patient to the hospital. But normally ambulances will be ordered from the hospital. Such a procedure should reduce mileage and make more economical use of each vehicle and driver. We envisage that all 'B' hospitals should be connected to their health centres and to 'A' hospitals by radio.[4]

It does not follow that the hospitals which are at present the largest should be the first to be considered for development as 'B' hospitals. One of them is in fact already earmarked for development as a 'Regional' hospital (something

[4] See Chapter 5.

mid-way between our categories 'A' and 'B') in the Ministry's development plan. Selection for development as a 'B' hospital should take account of such factors as the hospitals' current work load, pressure on beds, population density, industrial developments, communications and the proximity of other good hospitals. Similar criteria should apply to both voluntary and government hospitals. While it is desirable for such hospitals to be at or near district administrative centres, this need not be an overriding consideration. It is, however, essential that the pace of hospital development and health unit development should be kept closely in step. A 'health area' must be developed as a whole.

The rate of progress in developing 'B' hospitals as integral parts of health areas will inevitably depend on the availability of finance for current costs and on the training of the requisite staff, as well as on the costs of construction. By upgrading some hospitals and by enlarging others, it should be possible to reach a target of twenty-six in this category by 1980. It is estimated that the recurrent cost of such a hospital would be about £90,000 per annum. We suggest that twenty-six hospitals up-graded to this level (and assuming the closure or down-grading of some redundant units) might add £0·7 million per annum to the cost of the Health Service.[5]

The twenty-six 'B' hospitals would themselves account for (say) 6,000 beds. Adding to this 2,000—a conservative estimate—for beds in 'A' hospitals (including Princess Margaret) and the larger voluntary or other hospitals remaining (including Tanga) gives 8,000 beds in good general hospitals, distributed according to population and communications. This would amount to one bed per 1,875 for a population of 15,000,000 in 1980. To this may be added the 4,000 'holding' beds at health centres which brings the ratio of beds with resident medical supervision down to 1 per 1,250 of the population. These ratios take no account of the beds in mental and other special hospitals and in the remaining voluntary 'hospitals' which are not grant-aided.

---

[5] See Appendix B. The cost of the government hospital services outside Dar es Salaam is estimated to have been about £1·7 million in 1961.

If it should prove impossible to achieve twenty-six 'B' hospitals by 1980, it would be better to develop fewer hospitals of the quality we have indicated than to multiply at a lower standard. It is essential that the development of health units and hospitals should be kept in step. The success of the whole plan depends as much upon the calibre of the supporting hospitals as on any other factor. If the hospitals are to meet the new demands which the expanding services in the rural health centres will undoubtedly create, they must operate at great pressure. The fewer of these hospitals there are, and the further each is from an 'A' hospital to which it can refer its difficult problems, the greater this pressure will be.

The category 'A' hospital with 500 beds or more will serve as the local general hospital for its area as well as acting as a reference hospital for a number of health areas. It should have a fully qualified consultant staff in the major clinical divisions and in anaesthetics as well as special units in some of the following: paediatrics, psychiatry, ophthalmology, orthopaedics, otolaryngology and dental surgery. It should have well equipped pathology and X-ray departments under consultant direction.

Each 'A' hospital should act as a postgraduate training centre. In particular, medical officers must be trained to man the 'B' hospitals competently in one or more of the major clinical disciplines of medicine, paediatrics, surgery, and obstetrics. For this purpose registrarships and clinical assistantships should be established, the latter to be available for medical officers who have worked for a period in a 'B' hospital and wish to return to an 'A' hospital to keep in touch with advances in their subjects, or to work for special qualifications. The 'A' hospital will be the normal place for the pre-registration training of newly qualified medical graduates. It will set the standards for the 'B' hospitals within reach of it, and consultants will visit these hospitals to consult, advise and teach in their specialities. The possibility of giving specialist advice when requested, by means of the radio communication system we envisage, should also be considered. Its nursing and technician establishment must, therefore, be sufficient not only for patient service but also for training. As well as having a school of nursing it will be a training centre for laboratory technicians and radiographers, and for medical auxiliaries selected for training in special departments (such as anaesthetics, theatre work, ophthalmology, dentistry).

What we mean, therefore, by an 'A' hospital is something more ambitious than the 'regional' hospital envisaged in the Ministry's current development plan. We think it essential for training facilities and consultant services to be made available in more than one centre, if only to provide the 'B' hospitals with the help and support they need. Each centre should be self-sufficient in qualified consultant staff and should have a nursing establishment and equipment appropriate to a hospital of its size.

Provided there are enough 'B' hospitals of the requisite quality, there need not be more than three 'A' hospitals. More than this cannot be afforded. At present, the only hospital besides the Princess Margaret which approaches this category in terms of number of beds is Tanga (410 beds, 1961). This hospital is, however, far below 'A' standards in most other respects. The current development plan envisages Mwanza hospital expanding from 220 to 370 beds in the next few years. We do not believe that this will be large enough to enable it to operate as an 'A' hospital with the functions we have named. We should like to see Mwanza, with its Medical Research Institute and good communications, becoming a hospital of the size and stature of the Princess Margaret Hospital. The establishment of an alternative focal point for training in the west of the country 600 miles from Dar es Salaam would be an important advantage for recruitment of all grades of staff. It would also have the merit of spreading more widely the benefits of high standards of training and supervision. As regards the third 'A' hospital we do not wish to make any definite recommendation, though we expect that the appropriate location will probably be somewhere in the north of the country.

The Hospital Services

We recommend that the distinction which we have made between 'A' hospitals and 'B' hospitals should be rigidly applied. Inevitably there will be demands for more and more beds at 'B' hospitals. But the expansion of hospital facilities should be along the lines which we have indicated. A hospital of much more than 250 beds grows beyond the capacity of a non-specialist staff. But until it reaches about 500 beds it is not an economical unit to staff and equip as a consultant reference hospital. The distinction by size and function between categories 'A' and 'B' should be kept clear-cut. A hospital of intermediate size is neither one thing nor the other. Facilities should be expanded by opening new 'B' hospitals until each area has its own hospital. At that stage it might be appropriate to open a fourth 'A' hospital.

The Special Hospitals

There are at present in Tanganyika hospitals for obstetrics (Dar es Salaam), infectious diseases (Dar es Salaam), tuberculosis (Kibongoto and Mbeya), mental disease (Dodoma and Korogwe) and a number of leprosy institutions (Chazi, Makete and Baraka). There are no geriatric or children's hospitals or institutions for the physically disabled.

The special branches of clinical medicine are becoming increasingly dependent upon each other's resources and upon laboratory and X-ray facilities which are expensive to duplicate. For these reasons there is a trend throughout the world for isolated specialist hospitals to be replaced by specialized departments within general hospitals or by units within a closely integrated hospital group. There is every reason for Tanganyika to follow this trend. The obstetric and infectious diseases hospitals are in fact already administered as units of the Dar es Salaam hospital group, and we understand that the former will eventually be moved to the site of the Princess Margaret General Hospital.

The leprosy hospitals consist of small units of fifty beds or less which are relatively isolated from other hospital facilities. In Tanganyika and elsewhere, the present trend is for more and more of the treatment for leprosy to be undertaken on an out-patient basis at special clinics, health

131

centres or hospitals and sometimes at treatment centres with residential facilities available on an open village or settlement pattern. Remedial surgery and acute medical care is undertaken in general hospitals. Thus, the only role we see in the future for specialized leprosy units is to provide for those persons who are severely disabled in small institutions.

The government's tuberculosis hospital at Kibongoto (302 beds), the American Baptists' tuberculosis hospital at Mbeya (104 beds), the Lutheran long-stay mental hospital at Korogwe (Lutindi, 140 beds) and the government mental hospitals at Dodoma (Mirembe, 746 and Isanga, 246 beds) are all self-contained units. At Mbeya, Korogwe and Dodoma there are small government general hospitals within reach of the special hospitals. Kibongoto tuberculosis hospital is more isolated, twenty-five miles from the nearest general hospital at Moshi (263 beds).

While the trend in Europe is for more and more sanatorium beds to be empty every year, the number of patients under treatment for pulmonary tuberculosis in Tanganyika has risen enormously in the last fifteen years. There are known to be many more cases not under medical care, and the problem is growing. Although out-patient treatment of pulmonary tuberculosis is being undertaken with increasing success, there are not enough hospital beds to provide for the early weeks of initial assessment and treatment and for relapsed and complicated cases.

The right policy is to provide the necessary beds at the general hospitals. There is no case for the creation of any more special hospitals. Cases of non-pulmonary tuberculosis and complicated and surgical pulmonary cases certainly require the facilities of the general hospital. For other patients less elaborate accommodation and equipment and less intensive nursing is required than in other wards of the general hospital and the cost of building and maintaining the tuberculosis wing should be correspondingly less. If there are good bacteriological facilities, and satisfactory accommodation for out-patients suffering from tuberculosis is available and there is an effective organization for supervised treatment and follow-up at surrounding health centres, the staff of the general hospital and the local health services can between them deal effectively with pulmonary tuberculosis close to the patients' homes.

Kibongoto hospital has established a unique reputation. Although it is not ideally situated if judged by modern criteria, it is well placed for the large population it serves. With its satellite clinics it can be expected to continue to meet a need in the Kilimanjaro area for the foreseeable future. In addition, it can serve as a national centre for tuberculosis research, though here again it is at a disadvantage by reason of its limited laboratory facilities and its distance from a general hospital.

While there is little need for nearly all other types of special hospital, there is a case for special institutions for medium and long-stay mental patients. Nevertheless, such hospitals should be sited sufficiently near to good general hospitals to enable them to call upon their medical staff when necessary and to make use of their laboratory, X-ray and other facilities.

For the initial assessment of mental illness and for many short-stay mental cases and cases of psychoneurosis there should be facilities at the general hospitals themselves. We were therefore glad to learn that the government is planning to establish psychiatric holding units at district hospitals. We hope that this policy will be followed by the larger voluntary hospitals. Provision might vary from small holding units of two to four beds up to a full psychiatric unit of twenty to thirty beds at each 'A' hospital. Many of the acute psychotics referred to Mirembe Hospital are examples of transient toxic psychosis and recover in a few weeks. Many of them need not have been sent there had the referring doctor had some experience in the recognition of these toxic psychoses and had facilities been available for managing them at the general hospital. Still less should it be necessary to refer uncomplicated epilepsy to the mental hospital (as we find is commonly done). The care and rehabilitation of such patients is the business of the medical institution nearest the patients' homes.

It is inevitable in present conditions that many disturbed

persons will first come to the notice of the police and of the local chiefs. And where doctors and magistrates are scarce, the police cannot avoid taking responsibility for many mentally ill persons in the initial stages. But chiefs and police should be required to bring anyone believed to be seriously mentally ill to the nearest medical unit as soon as this can be arranged, and the practice of putting in prison people awaiting certification should be abolished as soon as possible.

The instruction of chiefs and police in this matter will be necessary and they should be given discretion to refer patients to a hospital at a distance if no medical opinion is available on the spot. Likewise, instruction in mental health and disease must be an important item in the training of the Tanganyikan medical practitioner both before and after he qualifies, so that the health centre can become the first place of reference for mental cases. More attention should also be paid to the subject of mental illness in the training of nurses who will be working outside as well as inside hospitals.

The success of the psychiatric holding units will depend on the provision at each hospital of a nucleus of trained mental nursing staff and a specially trained mental welfare worker. It will depend also on the interest of the hospital medical staff and on the availability of psychiatrists for consultation and periodic advisory visits. All medical staff should be encouraged to spend one or two months at a mental hospital or even to undertake a formal house appointment. The practitioners trained in Tanganyika should be required to reside there for a few weeks during their period of internship training.

The establishment of psychiatric holding units at government and voluntary general hospitals and the better orientation of doctors and nurses toward mental disorder will spare the mental hospital the admission of many patients who would be successfully treated near their own homes. And the referred mental patient should reach the hospital in better physical and mental condition than is now often the case. The existence of competent staff nearer home should make possible the earlier discharge of patients for further care and treatment on an ambulatory basis.

These holding units are unlikely, of themselves, to reduce the total load of work now undertaken (or attempted) at Mirembe Hospital. More enlightened attitudes and a greater awareness of the value of medical treatment will result in more patients being brought to hospitals for treatment, and to this process the educational work of the health centres will undoubtedly contribute. Already in ten years, admissions to Mirembe have increased fourfold. This trend may be expected to continue, but we hope less steeply. And if the general hospitals cope successfully with the minor and short-stay acute cases, the proportion of seriously ill and intractable patients reaching Mirembe will be higher and the work to this extent heavier.

We cannot escape the conclusion that more than two psychiatrists and more than one mental hospital are needed. Not only is Mirembe Hospital insufficient because its 750 beds are not enough for the country's needs, it is insufficient because the psychiatric service is so completely centralized and thereby remote from the homes of the great majority of its patients. The participation of the general hospitals along the lines discussed above would certainly be a great step in the direction of decentralization. But we believe that at least one more mental hospital is needed now. As about half of the patients reach Mirembe via Dar es Salaam, this would be the obvious place to establish a second mental hospital.[6] The facilities of Princess Margaret Hospital would be available to assist the new hospital and training could be concurrently provided for general medical and nursing staff in this essential branch of medicine.

As with all other consultants and specialists, it should be an important part of the psychiatrists' work to visit the general hospitals for consultations and to advise on the running of the holding units. The establishment of psychiatrists should therefore be sufficient to make this possible without detriment to the running of the mental hospitals. In addition, there is the inevitable court work which means much (clinically unproductive) time away. So far as possible ways

---

[6] We are informed that such a hospital is included in the current Development Plan, has been designed and building is about to start.

should be found to relieve psychiatrists of time-consuming administrative commitments so that they can devote themselves to clinical work and training. All that is said on this subject of administrative duties in relation to general hospitals applies equally here.

Our proposals for improvements in the services for the mentally ill will involve important changes in existing training courses and the development of new courses. These are discussed more fully in Chapter 10. A cadre of mental welfare assistants is especially needed if the best use is to be made of the hospital psychiatric service. Highly trained psychiatric social workers are not essential in the present stage of development. A beginning could be made by sending suitably selected staff overseas, so that they can train others locally on their return and arrange in-training courses for nursing orderlies and other mental hospital workers. Occupational therapy also needs to be developed and staff recruited or trained for this. It is to be hoped that teaching facilities at Makerere in psychiatry, both undergraduate and postgraduate, will be developed soon and that research in problems of mental health and disease will be supported and encouraged in East Africa, as is now being done most successfully under Professor Lambo in West Africa. With the output of the Makerere Medical School increasing there may be expected to be more doctors interested in this branch of medicine. It is important that one mental hospital at least in Tanganyika should be brought up to the standard required to offer postgraduate training at house officer and registrar level.

These are our main proposals for the reorganization and development of the hospital services. What is required is a concentrated and integrated structure for the whole of the country with a high standard of staffing, and providing a high level of service and support for the area health centres and clinics. The administrative means by which this can be achieved are discussed in the next chapter, and staffing requirements are dealt with in Chapter 9.

7 The Administrative and Financial Structure

A sound administrative structure will be required to carry out effectively the reorganization and continuing development of the personal health and hospital services which we have recommended in preceding chapters. Tanganyika is, however, short of administrative skills and trained administrators at every level of health service administration. This shortage is, moreover, made worse by a complicated division of health service responsibilities between central, local and regional government and the voluntary agencies.

In Chapter 2 we described the role which different organizations at present perform. The hospitals are provided by the central government and the voluntary agencies: the latter own nearly half the beds. The out-patient and dispensary services of the voluntary agencies and the central government deal with broadly the same number of attendances, but the total of both combined is substantially less than the number attending local authority services. The division of work between central and local government in respect of these initial consultation services arises from the fact that the former provides the services in the towns and the latter in the rural areas. No general principle determines, however, the distribution of work between the local authorities and the voluntary agencies.

In the hospital, dispensary and maternity and child welfare services there is considerable overlap and duplication between central government, local government and the voluntary agencies. This much is clear from what we have already written. Tanganyika cannot afford this misuse of scarce resources. Moreover, the existing distribution—or maldistribution—of services is preventing the development of an effective system of reference of patients from the initial attendance stage to the hospital; it encourages patients to go direct to hospitals and thus diverts hospitals from performing their proper functions; its complexity and lack of co-ordination contributes to the ineffectiveness of supervision of auxiliary and subordinate staff, and for these and other reasons professional skills are undertaking duties which lay administrators should be handling.

In the recommendations we have so far made we have laid great stress on these matters of principle: on the need for a system of referral; on the importance of supervision; and on the proper use of professional and administrative skills. To apply these principles calls for a general unification of all the services and the shaping of a simple chain of referral, supervision and administration. These requirements are made even more necessary by our proposals for the step-by-step development of local health and hospital areas during the next twenty years. Un-coordinated and patchwork developments will misuse resources. The country must not in the future haphazardly concentrate some resources in some areas and other resources in other areas. It must not push the development of certain services in particular areas too far ahead of their supporting links. It must not train subordinate staff and appoint them to particular posts if they cannot be adequately supervised. It cannot afford expensive equipment—however generously donated from abroad—if the resources are not available for its maintenance.

Guided by these principles, and by a desire to see more effective use being made of the dedicated work of those who at present staff the services, we attempt in this chapter to outline a system of unified planning and policy-making which, in our opinion, is likely to make better use of available resources. In much of what we say here and elsewhere we are very conscious of the fact that we are saying very little that is new to the senior officials of the Ministry. But we hope we are writing for a wider public. We discuss first the role of the local authorities and then the role of the voluntary agencies. Two final sections of the chapter are concerned with working out, in practical detail, the principle of unifying the government and voluntary agency services into an integrated programme of medical care. They relate, first, to the structure of grant-aid from government to the voluntary agencies; second, to the need for uniformity in the charges for in-patient and out-patient care.

Apart from operating the environmental services in the towns, the principal role of the local authorities in the health field is to provide the dispensary and maternity and child welfare services in the rural areas. These are the services which we have singled out in Chapter 5 for the most rapid development and most radical change. All our recommendations for these services are designed to increase greatly the application of preventive medicine and health education and to integrate these responsibilities with the curative work of the health clinics and health centres.

The creation of an integrated service has been advocated for many years—as we have pointed out in Chapter 1. Despite the enthusiastic acceptance of this policy at medical headquarters, only twenty-two health centres have so far been established. One reason for this slow rate of progress has obviously been financial. But this has not been the only reason. While the need for integrating preventive and social medicine is fully comprehended at medical headquarters, such a service is still regarded as something of a luxury by public opinion in general, and by local councillors in particular. There are, of course, some important exceptions, but in general it is true to say that local authorities have done extremely little to add preventive services to their existing responsibilities. Nor is this surprising. Such is the burden of suffering caused by the formidable host of endemic diseases which we have described in Chapter 3 that it is hard to expect district councillors to take a longer-term view of the needs of their community and of the importance of prevention.

In other circumstances we might have favoured making local government responsible for all the local health services in the hope of enlisting the support of the leaders of local opinion. In view, however, of the extreme scarcity of resources which are locally available for health services, the prior claim of education which represents the greatest challenge to local government, and the present lack of specialized administrative skills at the local level, we do not think it desirable (except possibly in the large towns) to leave these health responsibilities in the hands of local authorities even with extensive central government grants and systematic inspection. We have studied carefully Mr. Kent's recommendations on these matters.[1] We do not, however, believe that they should be implemented now or in the immediate future.

We do not take this view solely because of a fear that local authorities will fail to give adequate attention to preventive work. There are other cogent reasons which led us to this decision. First, the efficiency of the local health services depends to a considerable extent upon close co-operation with the voluntary agencies. Not only are there serious geographical and administrative obstacles to co-operation, but we anticipate much friction arising between the local authorities and these agencies: we have come across instances where serious antipathy is already evident at the local level. Second, we are anxious to promote health education at the health centres and we are convinced that this is not likely to be successful unless there are strong links with the self-help and village development committees. At the present stage of local political development, this seems to us of the greatest importance in the task of raising standards of living in the rural areas.

Third, and perhaps most significant of all, is the question of the competence of local government in the special field of medical care. We are very conscious that there are parts of the country where local government is at a very early stage of development. Many of the new councillors have had virtually no experience of government or of committee work in the health field. They have yet to learn about the general

---

[1] Kent, A. W. *Report on the Services to be Administered by Local Authorities in Tanganyika and Consequential Financial Arrangements*, 1962.

role of the elected representative as distinct from that of the official—quite apart from all the simpler lessons concerning the proper management of public funds and the appointment of staff. It is not only councillors who lack experience. Many of the officials too have had few opportunities to learn their functions and have, therefore, commanded little or no authority in any attempts they may have made to guide their councils. In the autumn of 1962, it was clear that the system of local government had virtually broken down in some parts of the country.

We are not attempting to generalize from this experience which we regard as essentially transitional, but it is certainly not the time to load new responsibilities for the planned development of a unified service on to the shoulders of local councillors. The health centres which we want to see extended on a nation-wide basis represent more complex administrative units than the few centres which have so far been developed; we would expect a more even level of administrative competence if control was in the hands of central government than if this responsibility were in the hands of local government. Control by central government would certainly be more popular with the professional staff. We noted that in many areas the morale of qualified staff employed by local authorities was extremely low. Part of the unsatisfactory relationships between employer and employee was due to the financial difficulties facing some authorities: money was simply not available to pay for adequate and, in some cases, any supplies of drugs. In such circumstances it is not surprising that those who find themselves providing useless drugs to the sick take a less than charitable view of their employers. No personal service can work efficiently with a staff which is disgruntled and discontented. This is a further reason for taking the service under the direct control of the central government.

We are aware that a small number of authorities have shown themselves to be well able to run health centres and dispensaries and will resent the loss of these services to the central government. In such circumstances exceptions might be made. But we do not imagine that the majority of authorities will oppose the change with any great energy. The control and development of primary education is absorbing the time, energy and financial resources of most councils: this is a vitally important responsibility which is in essence simpler to discharge.

While we recommend that all *personal* medical and health services[2] should be made the responsibility of the central government, this will not leave the local authorities without any duties in the broad health field. They will remain responsible for the *environmental* health services— water, sewage, street cleansing, slaughter houses, refuse disposal, housing, etc. They have not given adequate attention to these matters in the past and we strongly urge in Chapter 8 that serious efforts be made to raise the whole level of the environmental and sanitary services. District councils will be required to form public health committees, to propose and effect bye-laws and to see that they are enforced. Where an appropriate committee has been formed and the legislation prepared, we recommend that the health inspectors should be transferred to the control of the district council. Meanwhile, as a temporary arrangement, they should continue to operate from health centres and be responsible to the central government.

We hope that local authorites will appreciate the importance of the role they are asked to play in the protection and promotion of the collective health of their communities. The maintenance of a sanitary environment is a task somewhat lacking in glamour possibly because its impact on the health of the people is indirect. But we would remind any authorities who feel slighted by our proposals that in the battle against many of the principal diseases of Tanganyika, more can be achieved by the spray gun, the panga and the hoe than by the indiscriminate use of the hypodermic needle. We explain in more detail in the next chapter the programme of work awaiting local authorities.

We have now given a number of reasons in support of our

---

[2] All services provided for identifiable individuals as distinct from environmental and other impersonal services which benefit groups or communities.

recommendation that henceforward the central government should assume responsibility for directing, controlling and supervising all the health and medical services financed by government. Dominating all these reasons is the principle of unification on which we lay so much stress in this Report. If there is to be any improvement in the medical services provided for the mass of the people in the rural areas the principle must be applied at all levels. This leads us to discuss the future role of the voluntary agencies in the reorganized structure of health services.

The voluntary agencies as a whole have been even less active than the local authorities in developing an integrated preventive and curative service. Indeed, with the notable exception of maternity and child welfare work, they have hardly made any contribution. Preventive medicine is, after all, regarded in most countries of the world as the responsibility of government authorities rather than of voluntary bodies, and it has been natural for the voluntary agencies in Tanganyika to interest themselves almost exclusively in curative work. They have, moreover, seldom been given any encouragement, financial or otherwise, by central or local government to engage in preventive work. This has meant in practice that less attention tends to be paid to preventive work in those areas where the voluntary agencies are providing the principal curative services.

As we have already shown, the voluntary agency and government services have developed separately and independently of each other. Even more important, the twenty or so separate agencies have developed in a highly individual and independent manner. In some areas co-operation on an *ad hoc* basis has grown up, in many others it has not. In some parts of the country there is duplication of services, in others there are virtually no services at all. Duplication even takes the form of dispensaries in the same village or settlement or closely adjoining settlements. In a wealthier country duplication of this kind might be welcomed as an element of choice for patients and as a competitive spur to efficiency. It is extremely doubtful, however, whether this kind of development does in fact offer much real choice in terms of effective curative medicine; it is even more doubtful whether the country can afford such a misuse of resources. Moreover, there are many villages and settlements which lack any medical service, however primitive. In a great number of areas, patients have to walk twenty miles or more to reach the nearest dispensary. In such circumstances, duplication is undoubtedly wasteful.

This is not the only form in which waste occurs. Owing to the extremely low population density over much of the country, the task of visiting, supervising and supplying outlying dispensaries involves many hours of travelling time and costly wear and tear on the vehicles which have to be driven along the bumpy tracks of the rural areas. There are some parts of the country where the government chain of dispensaries is supplemented by one or more further and uncoordinated chains belonging to voluntary agencies of different denominations, each supervised and supplied by separate organizations. The furthest dispensary in the government chain may be far from any government hospital but close to a voluntary agency hospital which is manned by a perfectly competent medical officer. Providing that the medical officer has time to spare, it is no more than common sense to suggest that this government dispensary should be supervised from a voluntary hospital if it happens to be substantially nearer to it. Common sense has, however, yet to prevail in this respect in some areas of the country, with the result that travelling has become the principal activity of some medical officers, and would become the principal activity of others if the task of supervision were thoroughly performed. In one part of the country, despite frequent representations and generous subsidies, government and voluntary agency workers continue to cross and re-cross each other's paths as they visit leprosy treatment centres. In view of the shortage of medical staff which will continue for many years to come, it is essential that there should be no wasted man-hours and vehicle-hours in unnecessary journeys.

If there is to be any improvement in these matters in the short run, it must come in part from closer co-operation between voluntary agency doctors and government doctors than has occurred in the past in many areas. Closer co-operation is also needed between the government and the voluntary agencies in the field of hospital services. Indeed, such co-operation is of critical importance in view of the large role of the voluntary agencies in the hospital services of Tanganyika—larger than in Uganda, Kenya or Rhodesia —and in view also of the particular nature of the recommendations we have made in Chapter 6 for the development of the hospital services. In recent years the government has, by grant formulas and other means, been able to influence the location of several new voluntary agency hospitals. But there are still several voluntary hospitals which are not sited where they are most needed. There has also been a tendency for the proliferation of small and inefficient units. About 40% of the beds in voluntary hospitals and dispensaries combined are not supervised regularly by a medical practitioner.

We are convinced that the time has come for Tanganyika to develop an integrated health service, which conforms to a national plan which should be laid down from the centre and which observes a set of principles determined on a national basis. This is essential for reasons of economy, and for the success of the phased or step-by-step development of interdependent hospitals, health centres and clinics which we have recommended. Only by planning can scarce administrative and professional staff be used to the best advantage. The country cannot afford to have dispensaries in competition with one another, badly sited hospitals, under-utilized resources in one place and no resources in another, doctors who cross each other's paths and who spend too much time in travelling for administrative purposes, expensive equipment and no trained staff in one centre, and trained staff with no equipment in another, and so on.

The maximum use of all medical resources can, we believe, be achieved without resort to nationalization. To do so, however, will require a great deal of co-operation and goodwill on every side. From all we have learnt during our travels to many parts of the country we are assured that many of the voluntary agencies are willing to co-operate as closely as possible with the government in its policy-making and planning functions. Planning does not mean uniformity in every respect. Some areas will progress faster than others. This is as it should be. Indeed, it is what we recommend. And there must be room and opportunities for experiments of every kind. By planning we do not, therefore, mean the centralization of every decision. On the contrary, we would urge the need for devolution of responsibility within an over-all plan as this is essential for flexibility. The Ministry of Health effects at present a considerable devolution of authority within its own services. All we are suggesting is that the same system should be extended when the government plays a more active part in the affairs of the voluntary agencies and takes responsibility for the dispensary and health centre services. For those agencies who are ready to take part in a unified service we therefore propose a revised system of grant-aid from the central government. This is described later.

In drawing up these proposals for grant-aid, we gave considerable thought to the role which the voluntary agencies can most appropriately play within the health services of the country. In Chapter 5, we described in detail our proposed system of health units. It is a system which depends upon the closest team work, constant supervision, and continual liaison with the local agents of health education and community development. Frankly, we do not believe that the voluntary agencies can play an effective part within these services nor do we imagine that they really wish to do so. The regular system of supervision and the day-to-day co-ordination of functions with national and local activities —both of which we regard as essential to the successful working of our proposals—are not consistent with the kind of independent action which is the great strength of a voluntary agency. A health unit cannot be given very general terms of reference and told to interpret them in any way it thinks best. A health unit must be a platoon playing its part in a national campaign under the guidance of the epidemiological service. This is one of the many reasons for taking these local services out of the hands of local government. It is also a reason for suggesting to the voluntary agencies that they withdraw from this particular field of activity as government services develop to take their place.

While we suggest that the voluntary agencies withdraw from the provision of dispensary services, we also suggest that they be asked to extend their hospital services so that they can continue to play a vital part in a developing national hospital plan. The general principles behind this plan were outlined in Chapter 6. We believe that these principles will be acceptable to all concerned and we hope that the voluntary agencies will be prepared to participate to the full in this essential development.

It has long been recognized by leaders of opinion in the voluntary agencies that hospital planning cannot be expected to emerge from the separate action of over twenty independent agencies on the one hand, and central and local government which is inadequately informed of the agencies' plans on the other. The government and the agencies have been moving into closer partnership in recent years. We make proposals later in this chapter aimed to effect a marriage or, for those agencies who think it more appropriate, a platonic relationship.

The policy of concentrating resources on a few large units carries with it the corollary that some of the present grant-aided voluntary hospitals must in time cease to be hospitals under the plan, and thus cease to be eligible for grant-aid. We do not recommend a sudden withdrawal of grants but rather a process of tapering spread over five years to enable the agency concerned to readjust its activities to the new circumstances. It may wish to continue to provide limited hospital services without the aid of grants. Alternatively, it may wish to concentrate its resources on those hospitals which have been designated under the plan, or in other ways. Some of the present small 'hospitals' operated by voluntary agencies may be suitable for adaptation as health centres and might be relinquished by agreement to form part of the government's health unit system.

If there is to be a closer relationship between the central

147

11

government and the voluntary agencies, there need also to be improvements in the structure of administration and policy-making both within the Ministry and among the voluntary agencies. The concentration of the local authority personal health services under the direct administration of the Ministry represents a substantial increase in responsibilities : in addition, the Ministry will have to play in the future a more positive role in planning the health services of the country. These enlarged functions justify a Ministry with exclusive responsibilities for health. As we were completing our Report at the end of 1962, we were glad to learn that this decision had been taken by the government.

The changes which we would like to see on the voluntary agency side are equally important. At present the decisions of their Medical Advisory Committee are binding on no one : there is no central policy-making body representative of the voluntary agencies which can speak with any formal authority. The establishment of such a committee (a Voluntary Agency Planning Committee)[3] by the grant-aided agencies is essential for effective planning; moreover, we believe that unity and co-operation are in the agencies' best interests. A wholly representative and executive body, in place of the present Advisory Committee, would carry more weight in discussions with the government, particularly in hammering out a national plan for the hospital services.

This recommendation concerns the grant-aided agencies alone. Consultation with the government is no less essential for agencies which are not grant-aided. We hope that they will always seek advice and discussions with the Ministry of Health before embarking on new additions and extensions to their medical services. We hope too that they will adapt their present services to conform to national plans. Not to do so at this stage in Tanganyika's history would, we believe, be regrettable. We think the time has come, therefore, for the establishment of a Consultative Committee. This should be composed of representatives from these particular agencies and one or two senior officials of the Ministry. Initially, it would have two functions. It would

[3] See Organizational Chart, Appendix A.

serve as a forum for information and discussion on the planned development of the medical services of these agencies. Secondly, it should consider the need to strengthen existing legislation in respect to public health and the control of infectious diseases in the hospitals and other institutions maintained by the non-grant-aided agencies. These latter functions are, in any event, the responsibility of government and amending legislation will, we are assured, be required if they are to be effectively carried out.

Financial Assistance and Grants to the Voluntary Agencies
We do not propose to specify in precise detail the nature of the changes which should be made to the grant structure. We are content to lay down the main principles. In any event, we foresee that further changes will be required from time to time as circumstances alter and different stages of development are brought into effect. What we propose, therefore, applies only for a number of years. When certain phases of our plan are in operation the grant-aid regulations will require further revision to encourage developments in the next stage. The new Voluntary Agency Planning Committee, which we hope will be created, and the new hospital boards of management and advisory committees which we propose, will have important parts to play in this process of development.

For those voluntary agencies who wish to apply for grant-aid in respect of hospitals which are designated under the plan, we propose a choice of systems. We shall call these Scheme I and Scheme II. The former envisages the government taking over financial responsibility for the services in question, whilst preserving the religious character and traditions of the agency. The latter offers a new structure of grants and subsidies designed to help those agencies with substantial resources to adapt their services to the needs of the country.

Scheme I
Under this Scheme the government will assume full financial responsibility for the hospital or other approved

services. An agreement will be drawn up between government and the voluntary agency containing such conditions as are mutually agreed upon by the Minister and the agency concerned. These conditions should include :

   (i) A Board of Management of five persons should be established for each hospital (or group of hospitals); two being nominated by the voluntary agency, two by the Minister of Health, and one being nominated jointly by the local authority and the community development committee of the area in which the institution is sited. At least one member of the Board should be medically qualified. We shall be making similar recommendations for the government hospitals in Chapter 10.

  (ii) To preserve the religious character and traditions of the institution, the Chairman of the Board should be one of the nominees of the voluntary agency.

 (iii) The institution should retain its internal autonomy but its management should be subject to the general policy directives of the Ministry.

 (iv) The hospital may be required to carry out any or all of the functions of a government hospital of the same category—particularly the teaching, supervisory and clinical duties in respect to the local health services associated with the hospital.

  (v) The hospital will be required to pay the basic salary and wage scales adopted by the government.

 (vi) Institutions accepted by the Minister for inclusion in Scheme I will have to prepare annually their estimates of expenditure, including capital expenditure, for the following year. These estimates will be considered by the Minister, and if necessary amended. Subject to the provision of funds by the Legislature, any deficit will be met by government. The agency will, however, be required to subscribe towards the running costs of the institution not less than the average of what it subscribed during the three years before the introduction of the new regulations.

(vii) Accounts should be maintained in form and detail as required by the Minister and will be subject to government audit.

(viii) The charging of fees to patients for in-patient and out-patient services should be on the same basis as that applied in the government services (see below).

Scheme II

This scheme broadly follows the existing arrangements for grant-aid but makes a number of major changes in the structure of grants and the conditions attaching thereto, namely:

(i) The establishment of an Advisory Committee of five persons for each hospital (or group of hospitals). The Committee should be constituted on the same lines as the Board of Management described under Scheme I (i and ii).

(ii) The regulations governing the payment of staff grants[4] should be amended to provide for:

(a) Qualified local staff (Tanganyikan)[5]. As a condition of eligibility for any grant, government basis salary and wage scales must be introduced. In addition to the existing grants for these grades of staff, further grants will be payable representing the difference between current scales and the government salary and wage scales. These grants will only be paid if minimum supervisory professional, nursing, and technical staff (to be specified in regulations) has been provided by the voluntary agency. If these minimum supervisory conditions are not fulfilled the staff grants will be reduced to 75% and in some cases to 50%. To all

---

[4] The Medical (Grants-in-Aid to Missions) Regulations. General Notice No. 2297, 1955.
[5] This will require precise definition in the regulations.

these grants, increments should be added annually (at the appropriate rate ranging from 50 to 100%) on conditions to be specified in the revised regulations.

(b) Qualified expatriate staff.[6] A grant of 50% of the middle point on the government salary scale will be payable for all approved senior staff, namely, doctors, matrons and nursing sisters, and all qualified hospital technicians.

(iii) In view of the more generous staff grants, the bed grants for all institutions will be gradually withdrawn over a period of three years.

(iv) Certain further changes will be called for in the regulations governing the maximum grant-earning establishment for each hospital to bring them into line with our recommendations in Chapter 6.

(v) Qualified staff at grant-earning hospitals will be allowed, in approved cases, to be employed at training centres for medical aids, nurses, maternity aids and other categories of staff as approved by the Minister.

(vi) Certain categories of qualified staff, Tanganyikan and expatriate, may be approved for specified duties for grant-earning purposes from time to time by the Minister. In particular, arrangements may be made in appropriate cases for qualified medical staff to undertake, at negotiated rates, sessional duties at government health clinics and health centres for clinical and teaching purposes.

(vii) The present scale of grants for training purposes will need to be revised to take account of our recommendations in Chapter 9 in respect to the number and categories of trained staff required under development plans. In cases where training grants are no longer justified, they should be tapered off over a period of three years.

(viii) It will be a condition of the acceptance of these Scheme II proposals that our recommendations in

[6] This will require precise definition in the regulations.

respect of charges for in-patient and out-patient treatment be applied. (See below.)

(ix) All grants paid to voluntary agencies under this Scheme must be applied to the purposes for which they have been approved.

(x) Accounts and statistics should be submitted to the Ministry each year in a prescribed form. At present the information available from voluntary agencies is less than adequate for planning purposes.

It will not be possible to introduce all these changes by way of new regulations immediately and on the same date. For example, not all the changes we recommend in respect to the levying of charges can be applied until an adequate system of referral has been organized in a particular area. The timing of these various recommendations will need careful examination by the Ministry. And, as we have already pointed out, they will call for revision in the light of changing circumstances.

We recognize fully that our proposals under Scheme II will affect different agencies in different ways. An agency which was already paying local staff as much as the government would gain little or nothing at present (but some benefit in the future) from the new staff grants: those which are levying substantial out-patient charges will eventually suffer a loss of revenue. And all agencies which are at present receiving bed grants will eventually lose them. Thus, some agencies will be worse off than at present under Scheme II, others will be better off. These gains and losses will not, however, all happen at once. Unfortunately, the information is not available to allow us to calculate how many agencies will fall into each category, and for what period. We are, however, proposing these changes for the primary reason that the grant regulations must be made consistent with the general strategy of development for the health services as a whole. And it is also necessary to ensure that the conditions of service of locally paid staff are brought up to the national level, and that every encouragement is given to the improvement of the hospital services. Agencies which lack the financial resources to provide a service of the requisite standard under Scheme II will be able to participate under Scheme I.

The Minister, after discussion with the Voluntary Agency Planning Committee, must have the right to withhold or withdraw after due notice any grants payable under Scheme I and II for any of the following reasons:

(a) if satisfied that the conditions for approval of a grant are no longer being fulfilled;

(b) if satisfied that a voluntary agency is not treating patients of all denominations and creeds without discrimination, or is placing any patient under an obligation to receive religious instruction;

(c) if satisfied that regulations and syllabuses as approved by the duly constituted training bodies are not being complied with;

(d) if satisfied that such records, accounts and returns as are or may be prescribed by regulations are not kept in a satisfactory manner or are not submitted in accordance with the regulations.

In putting forward these recommendations for revising the structure of grant-aid and for our new proposals under Scheme I, we have attempted to combine a number of objectives. First, to unify and rationalize all the medical services and to make the most economical use of all such resources in the interests of the people of Tanganyika. Second, to provide uniformity in the method of levying charges at all institutions. Third, to accord equality of treatment for all qualified local staff working in voluntary institutions. Fourth, to encourage the promotion and training of supervisory staff recruited from the ranks of locally domiciled workers. Fifth, by making more generous contributions for staff and withdrawing grants for beds, to remove any incentive for the voluntary agencies to provide beds which are not properly staffed. Lastly, to leave the voluntary agencies with incentives to recruit staff from overseas and to attract funds from every source for capital expenditure, repairs and maintenance, the feeding of patients in hospitals, and the provision of needed supplies and equipment. The case for the partnership between government and voluntary agency stands or falls on the continuation of generous support from donors at home and abroad to care for the sick and disabled people of Tanganyika.

Charges for Medical Care

The existing arrangements for charging fees, which we now have to consider for both in-patient and out-patient treatment, were described in Chapters 1 and 2. Looked at as a whole, the position is one of bewildering complexity. Moreover, in many cases the charges levied do not seem to us to be based on any considered principles or accepted criteria related to diagnosis, therapy and prevention. They may bear little or no relation to the services provided.

What concerns us particularly is that this complexity is becoming more serious. Different voluntary agencies are raising their charges and imposing new ones. Local authorities are also developing different charging systems. In the absence of any attempt to impose some semblance of uniformity it must be expected that within the next five to ten years the picture will be one of even greater confusion.

The problem was to some extent foreseen years ago by Dr. E. D. Pridie, the Chief Medical Officer to the Colonial Office, in his review of the medical policy for Tanganyika. In the White Paper in 1949, the concluding paragraph reads 'Dr. Pridie has advised that all patients except the indigent, should be charged for hospital treatment, whether in-patient or out-patient, and that similar charges should be levied by Native Administrations at rural medical stations under their control. The Government has given consideration to this suggestion and intends to bring in a scale of charges as soon as practicable.'[7]

The White Paper did not indicate how the indigent were to be identified in a country which lacked and still lacks any poor law service. Nor did it discuss the effects on the services provided by the voluntary agencies if charges were levied throughout the government system. The scale of fees and the policies of charging generally adopted by the volun-

---

[7] Sessional Paper No. 2, 1949.

tary agencies are in many cases only made possible by the existence of free government services for the very poor. It is clear, therefore, that Government must continue to make provision for those who cannot afford to pay.

In the discussions we have had with a large number of people, and from our examination of fee-charging systems in use or considered in Tanganyika, Kenya and Uganda,[8] there is clearly a major conflict of opinion. It was put to us by some that patients value treatment more highly if they pay for it. Hence, they are more likely to co-operate as patients. It was further argued that in view of the acute shortage of doctors, people should be discouraged from seeking advice and treatment for minor illnesses and conditions. It was said—and very forcibly in Dar es Salaam—that the curative services would break down in the absence of any control, by charges and by turnstile, over the many thousands of people of all ages and conditions thronging out-patient clinics. This statement we confirmed by observation.

The case for a comprehensive system of fee-charging is most cogently put in the Kent Report[9] and it seems unnecessary for us, therefore, to elaborate on it further. It is important to note, however, that in this Report, as in the Pridie Report of 1949, no proposals are made for any simple administrative device for defining those who are unable to pay for themselves and/or their families. In an attempt to find some such device, we examined the possibilities of using Tax Exemption Certificates or some variant of them. In the end, however, we were forced to admit defeat as others had done before us. We learnt that the system was in general not working, and in those areas where it was operating, the results were often unjust and entailed unfair discrimination. We came to the conclusion that it will be some years before this proposal could be seriously considered as a solution to the problem of defining the poor.

Those who argued against the levying of charges did so

---

[8] In particular, Uganda Protectorate, *Statement by the Protectorate Government on the Reimposition of Charges for Medical Treatment in Government Medical Units*, Sessional Paper No. 16 of 1958/59, Entebbe.
[9] Kent, A. W., *op. cit.*

for many reasons apart from the difficulty of identifying the poor in the absence of a poor law system. Charges for out-patient services would, it was said, discourage people from seeking advice and treatment—or continuing a course of treatment—for infectious disease, tuberculosis and many other conditions. It would also be difficult to establish discriminating services by treatment or by grade of doctor or medical auxiliary in health centres, clinics and dispensaries —particularly for the care of mothers and children. Any scheme of discrimination for out-patient services could cut across and confuse the need for preventive advice and treatment, and put a heavy premium on injections, pills and drugs. Moreover, it would be expensive to administer, and in a situation of scarce administrative skills any general fee charging system would be susceptible to grave abuses.

In all these discussions, which illuminated deep and sincerely held cleavages of opinion, three points emerged which seemed to us to be important. First, there was general agreement on the need for uniformity in policy and practice throughout all the medical services in Tanganyika—government and voluntary. No integrated system was possible without a solution on a national scale to the problem of charges.

Second, we were impressed by the statements that were made to us about the reasons why many people, without religious affiliations to the particular institution, nevertheless seemed to prefer to attend fee-charging voluntary agency hospitals and clinics. What was of vital importance to them was to see the same person whom they knew and who knew them. They were looking for and valued the personal element in medical care. In a society of rapid cultural change this attachment to the known—and in particular the known elements of western institutional medicine—is understandable. Nor is it peculiar to the changing ways of Tanganyika.

The expression of this attachment and the apparent preference by some people for voluntary agency medical services in those areas where choice is possible comes about, in our view, because of the generally greater stability of trained staff in such services. By contrast, the more frequent movement of staff in government and local authority centres leads to the introduction of strange people with different and often conflicting attitudes and practices. Quite apart from the question of charges, there seems to us to be an important principle here which needs to be applied in the development of the local health services. A determined effort will have to be made to improve continuity of care in these services and to provide more opportunities for staff to achieve both stability and promotion, and to be rewarded for their work in a particular community which they know.

Third, it was impressed on us that we could not consider the question of charges without taking account of the tax structure in rural areas. To quote from the Kent Report: 'In all districts the personal rate places a proportionately greater burden on the poorer members of the community than on those with greater wealth. This makes the tax a regressive one. . . . The present local tax structure is also inequitable in that in many districts income of both single and married women is completely disregarded for local taxation purposes.'[10]

Any health service charges for out-patient, clinic and dispensary services would have to be flat-rate if uniformity in all rural areas is accepted as a necessary condition for an integrated medical service. Nor, in general, could any flat-rate system take account of earnings and personal resources, size of family and dependants, and other circumstances. For the poorer groups in the community—for perhaps half of the rural population of Tanganyika—the imposition of such charges would mean an even heavier regressive burden of taxation. And as one informant put it: 'In return for a grossly unfair system of taxation, what does the Government provide for the rural population? Schools for less than a third of the children—for which payment often has to be made—and some broken down dispensaries.' While this statement may be something of an exaggeration in respect of certain parts of the country, it does illuminate the general problem.

---

[10] Kent, A. W., *op. cit.*, p. 47.

Basically, this is the problem of poverty and the incapacity of large sections of the population to bear any charges for medical care. A recent report to the government on wage levels provides evidence of the extent of malnutrition and the deplorable living standards of many wage-earners and their families in urban areas.[11]

In considering all these factors, medical, social and financial, we felt we could not shelve the problem—a natural inclination : the unification of the services depended on a solution being found. Moreover, if it is not found now the problem will be much harder to resolve in the future, for the reasons we have advanced.

On one point we were agreed at an early stage in our discussions. Charges could not be justified by the contribution they would make to the revenue. As is clearly demonstrated in the Uganda report,[12] any system of charging in the government service would involve administrative problems which are not only troublesome but also very costly to solve. To defray these administrative costs and make a significant contribution to the health budget, charges would have to be substantial. But the higher the level of charges the more numerous would be the categories calling for exemption or special treatment. The administrative machinery would thus be driven to more complex and costly devices. We are convinced that the scarce administrative talents of Tanganyika could be much better deployed in other activities than levying health charges, if the only purpose they were to serve was to raise revenue. Higher taxes would be a much cheaper and easier administrative way of finding more money for the health services.

A stronger case for charges can be based upon the need to limit the demands made upon certain sectors of the health services. The more cases any medical worker is expected to see and treat in a day, the less time can be given to each and the less the value of the service given. There can come a point at which the consultation is of no clinical value at all. The whole process is destructive of the stan-

---

[11] *Report of the Territorial Minimum Wages Board*, Dar es Salaam, 1962.
[12] Uganda Protectorate, *op. cit.*

dards which it is the aim of the training programmes to create. Under excessive pressure, staff becomes not only increasingly incompetent but also frustrated and demoralized. Some way has to be found to limit demand. This is already the position at Dar es Salaam. It may soon be the position in other centres where we have noted that the trained staff in the government service is not keeping pace with the increasing demand. Nor is there any likelihood of them doing so in the immediate future.

The problem is worse in hospital out-patient than in in-patient work—if only because bed numbers and floor space impose some limit on the number of patients who can be admitted. But there is, nevertheless, a need to restrict in-patient admissions which are not medically justified lest a demand builds up for an expansion of hospital facilities which would absorb a disproportionate share of the health budget. As the services are gradually improved and as more and more people express a need for medical care, all the services will come under heavy pressure. We look to charges as one means of limiting demand on certain sectors only of the health services.

We are well aware that the ability to pay charges is not related to the need for medical attention : indeed, those who can least afford to pay probably need it most. For this reason alone we would insist that charges should be modest in amount (except for special doctor's clinics when attendance is by appointment). For this reason also we recommend that one charge should give the right to free medicine and re-attendance for up to four weeks. In certain cases treatment should be allowed to extend beyond four weeks without further charge. A schedule should be drawn up of these diag-nosed diseases or conditions to which this extension should be automatically applied. (For example bilharzia, trypano-somiasis, tuberculosis and certain other infectious diseases; diabetes, epilepsy and other disorders requiring permanent continued medication; orthopaedic treatment.)

Ideally, we would want to provide wholly free care for those who are very seriously ill and those with communic-able and preventable diseases. But some patients have more than one disease. It would be retrograde to abandon the principle of treating the patient in favour of treating the disease. And, administratively, any such system would involve either the complications of refunds or the need to charge after rather than before treatment. We must also reject this possibility because of the excessive amount of discretion it would place in the hands of relatively junior staff.

It would be wrong in principle to make a charge for a service which was not of definite value to the patient. We did not think that the quality of medical attention at present given in the dispensaries justified the levying of charges. Nor is it likely to for many years to come. Few existing dispensaries are in fact faced with an excessive demand and the collection of the charges would be a considerable administrative burden on the staff quite apart from offering temptations for corrupt practices. Thus, we do not recommend the levying of charges in any unit smaller than a designated health centre. This has the advantage of providing a minimum initial consultation service available quite freely to the poor in both the towns and the rural areas.

Not every patient who attends the health centre or hospital as an out-patient should be required to pay a charge. The list of exemptions could easily become very long and complex : we have tried to keep it short and simple and have allowed a considerable element of flexibility. Free care should be available to children under school leaving age and for all ante-natal and post-natal patients referred from health clinics. The person in charge of the unit should be entitled to waive charges for emergency cases and for indigents who cannot reasonably be expected to travel to a free clinic. In saying this, we have to admit that we have not solved the problem of defining the indigent. There are some means by which a proportion may be simply identified and they will be expected to produce the evidence for exemption. Others will be known to the staff of the health centre or hospital. Those who are not or who cannot produce any evidence will have to be left to the discretion of the staff concerned. It is a conclusion we do not like, but until the Tax

Exemption Certificate system is made effective or some system of health insurance is developed we see no alternative. We also recommend that free care should be available at hospital to all cases referred from a health centre; thus, those known to be needing the higher quality services will be enabled to receive them without charge. It is important, therefore, that charges should not be levied until an adequate system of reference is in operation.

We recommend that government employees should not be exempt from these and the following proposals for charges. We hope they will appreciate that it is thoroughly undesirable for the civil service to be treated as or to be regarded as a specially privileged class among the population. Their exemption from charges may have had some relevance in the days of colonial rule but it is singularly inappropriate today.

We recommend the adoption of similar principles for in-patient care to those which we have outlined above for out-patient care. Thus, in-patient care at a health centre is free (with one exception) because the attention provided in such circumstances may not be such as to justify charging. The exception is in the case of 'normal' deliveries (deliveries which have not been referred for in-patient care for medical reasons). We are well aware that the typical home in Tanganyika is far from being an ideal place for confinement. But we regard this need as of lower priority than others. The beds available must be reserved for mothers where labour is likely to be complicated.

In-patient charges should be applied uniformly in all hospitals, government and grant-aided voluntary, designated as being of the requisite standard. The charge for the average standard of accommodation should be modest in amount and calculated on a daily basis subject to a maximum. A substantially higher charge should be levied for normal confinements. Those exempt from charges would be patients suffering from mental illness, certain specific communicable diseases, children under primary school-leaving age, women admitted for complications of pregnancy and childbirth and indigents (certified as such by a chief or other designated official or referred as such by a senior officer in the health service).

Substantially higher charges should be levied for the use of amenity beds : such charges should vary strictly according to the amenity available (privacy, special food, better toilet facilities, etc.); there should be no variation in the general standard for the hospital concerned in the quality of medical or nursing care provided to amenity patients. A thorough review of the present system of graded charges therefore needs to be undertaken. At all levels of amenity a much higher charge should be levied for normal confinements than for other amenity in-patients. These general increases in charges for amenity accommodation do not justify any increase in the amounts sanctioned in respect of the private practice fee privilege received by government medical officers (specified in Ministry of Health and Labour Circular No. 5 of 1962).

This system of charges should be operated uniformly in both government and grant-aided voluntary hospitals and health centres. The principle of uniformity must be applied here—as with out-patient services—if unification is to be brought about. It is, we would repeat, a condition of the receipt of grant aid.

Such are our proposals for charges. In conclusion it might be helpful to summarize the principles which underlie them. We have tried to create an incentive for people to use *first* the medical facility which is of lower quality while making it easier than at present for a patient to be referred to a service of higher quality : in the case of hospital out-patients the *referred* patient is given free attention. We have been stricter about charging for in-patient care than out-patient care as *good* in-patient care is extremely expensive to provide and must be used only when it is absolutely necessary. We have been stricter with normal deliveries than other categories of hospital care, as we are quite clear that such patients deserve lower priority. We have tried to keep the charging system as simple as possible : it would be so easy to make the regulations much too complicated to be understood by patients and by those who would have to administer them.

We have tried to devise a system of charges that will help to protect the hospitals and yet not obstruct the development of preventive medicine and health education.

Broadly, and in a more fundamental sense, by restraining demand in certain sectors our proposals aim at bringing better medical care to the rural population while creating a system of priorities for the seriously ill in all areas. We are thus applying in the health field the principles enunciated by the President, Dr. Julius Nyerere, on 24th May, 1961, in relation to the payment of school fees. 'Where you must pick and choose, where some children must go to school and others cannot go to school, those parents who can help in the education of their children should help. It is their duty to help.' Hence, so long as only a small proportion of the people have access to good quality medical services it is their duty to contribute to the cost.

Health Insurance

In the recommendations we have made for certain selective charges at hospitals and health centres we emphasized the need to fix those for out-patients at a modest level. It is clear from the Chesworth Report on Minimum Wages, and its examination of the facts of poverty in Dar es Salaam and other areas, that large numbers of families will find it very difficult to make even token payments.[13] The greater the extent of illness in a family, the greater will be the severity of the charge. The fact that sickness can simultaneously create a need for additional expenditures on medical care and reduce sources of income is among the principal reasons for the development of a variety of health insurance arrangements in many countries of the world. It is not, therefore, surprising that a demand for health insurance has arisen in Tanganyika. We fully expect this demand to grow in the years ahead.

Our terms of reference did not require us to consider the detailed problems of introducing and administering a compulsory scheme in Tanganyika. At the time of our visit in August, 1962, we learnt that the matter was being investi-

[13] op. cit.

gated by the Minister. Consequently, we confine our remarks to general principles and to certain matters which are closely related to our proposals for the development of the health services.

We have little doubt that at some point during the period we have been surveying—and sooner rather than later—it will be necessary to make a start with a health insurance scheme. It would probably be wise, in the initial stages, to restrict any such scheme to gainfully employed persons in designated areas of the country—those areas with substantial sections of wage-earners and, more important still, areas which have relatively well-developed medical services. We expect that the introduction of such a scheme, even if contributions were limited to employers, would result in heavier demands for medical attention. It would not be right, in our view, to introduce a scheme and to lead certain sections of the population to expect to claim better medical care if the resources and staff to meet such demands are not available. In general, then, the development of a health insurance scheme should march in step with area improvements in medical resources. It will clearly be a long time before these are adequate in all areas of a country as large as Tanganyika; hence our suggestion that a start could be made in designated areas.

It has been put to us that a contribution of three shillings per month by employers for those employing fifty or more persons could yield a revenue of over £500,000 a year. If this were regarded as an annual addition to the health budget—as we consider it certainly should be—it would clearly allow the Ministry of Health to speed up, in a variety of ways, the development of the health services. But for the next few years these extra funds could not, in themselves, produce more medical practitioners. We have mentioned earlier that there are now fewer trained doctors and auxiliaries in the organized services per head of the population than there were five years ago. With the growth of population and other factors the position could get worse in the next few years before it begins to get substantially better; before the new Tanganyikan practitioners emerge in numbers to augment the staff, and additional numbers of training courses are in operation and more auxiliaries are produced. Our proposals in this respect are outlined in Chapter 9.

It may, of course, be possible to use a health insurance scheme as a means of persuading employers to recruit foreign doctors to take care of the needs of their employees. The voluntary agencies may also be able to bring in more trained medical staff from abroad. By these means relief may come somewhat sooner than we have implied. But the point we wish to stress is that unless there is an increase in trained medical and/or auxiliary personnel, improvements in the services for insured persons could only be obtained by lowering the standard of service available to the rest of the population. This should not be allowed to happen.

The conclusion we reach is that if health insurance is found to be administratively practicable and desirable, it should be introduced *gradually* as the necessary trained manpower becomes available. Progress might well be on a geographical or area basis. When one area is reorganized and provided with our new health centres and clinics and with hospitals staffed at the standards we recommend, it would be appropriate to schedule that area for the introduction of both health service charges and for health insurance *on the same day*.

8   Environmental Health and
the Work of the Local Authorities

The improvement of health depends on both personal and environmental services. The balance in which they are needed varies from place to place. Environmental services are particularly important in the towns, partly because the concentration of population gives increased opportunity for the conveyance of disease, and partly because of the direct social and physical effects of urban concentration itself, over-crowding and the growth of slums.

The problems of urban concentration are increasing in Tanganyika largely because of the rapid and possibly accelerating migration of people to the towns. And migration is likely to continue. The growth of population in the rural areas is not matched by employment opportunities. Any improvement in rural health conditions which, in turn, may add to the rate of population growth, can have the effect of adding to the pressure of people in the towns and therefore to the creation of more slums. These evils may, consequently, counterbalance the effects of better health in the rural areas. It follows that the expansion of the urban population should be accompanied by a strengthening of urban health services—particularly environmental services. For this to be achieved, there must be a good Medical Officer of Health with ample powers and responsibilities, a strongly administered health service, a vigorous housing policy, and adequate financial provision for the environmental services.[1]

We have not made a detailed examination of the sanitary

[1] See Appendix B.

conditions of the city of Dar es Salaam from the public health point of view and cannot therefore speak of the adequacy of present arrangements. We consider that such an examination should be made of conditions both in this city and in Tanga and in the larger towns. The last enquiry was made in 1956 and, in view of its recommendations,[2] we think a further survey is now warranted.

In this chapter, we are chiefly concerned with conditions in the smaller towns and in the rural areas where environmental services are rudimentary or in some places nonexistent. The time has come for an effective rural service to be created to run parallel with the development of health centres and health clinics described in Chapter 5.

We have already recommended that the environmental services should eventually be administered by local authorities and for three essential reasons. First, they are closely related to local needs and to the other activities of local authorities. Second, the procedures for enforcing the law require democratic consent to be effective. Third, environmental services are divorced in nature, though not in purpose, from the curative services. In principle, it would be desirable for technical supervision also to be a local authority responsibility. This is not possible at present in all areas. Thus, we have recommended that technical supervision at area level and above should be provided by central government. (See Chapter 5.)

In recommending that the environmental services should eventually be made the responsibility of the local authority, we do not believe that all or even most local authorities will immediately throw themselves into this activity with enthusiasm. We do believe, however, that advances in this field depend on the elected authority responding to the needs and demands of the local population. In some areas at least, these needs are already being expressed, and we would expect demands for an improved environment to grow as a result of the activities of the self-help and community development movement.

Community support is as necessary to raising the level of

---

[2] *Township Sanitation Report*, Dar es Salaam, 1957.

environmental sanitation as it is to any other activity directed at local improvement. Many of the processes of sanitary improvement must first be carried out by the community, using its own labour and local materials, until the money is available to pay for the development of more sophisticated facilities and techniques. We believe that interest in the subject of environmental health will grow throughout the country once some local authorities make a start. If these early activities are adequately supported by the central government, and if they result in material improvements in the standards of health in the local community, other authorities will follow the example which has been set for them. People in different areas will begin to make comparisons and will demand similar improvements. Thus, more authorities will be expected to take an interest in sanitary affairs until these activities become generally widespread. At this stage, the government should pass compulsory legislation to bring the late-comers into step with the majority. This has generally been the way in which progress has been made in most countries. We hope that this process will develop rapidly in Tanganyika.

By these means the necessary staff and organization for effective environmental work will be created. In time, the organization should be extended, in close co-operation with the preventive activities of the health centres, to include special environmental campaigns directed at the control or eradication of such diseases as malaria, filariasis and schistosomiasis. In certain places particularly affected by some of these conditions, there is already strong local feeling that control measures should be undertaken, though the particular disease which is the object of concern varies from one locality to another. Once the machinery for action has been created, local campaigns against specific conditions can be encouraged, subject only to the maintenance of adequate technical and organizational standards. Government can play a significant part in establishing satisfactory standards by providing technical advice and material aid in those places where the need is strongly felt, and where the community has shown its willingness to participate in the suggested programmes. It may thus be expected that local schemes for the control of one or another of these diseases will develop in different parts of the country and that these schemes will, by their example, lead to the initiation of others. The ultimate objective is to secure nation-wide programmes of this kind. We believe that the essential framework for this development is the creation of basic environmental services and health units, with the added stimulus of a number of enterprising local authorities undertaking prototype schemes.

Environmental sanitation consists in the control of all those factors in man's physical environment which exercise, or may exercise, a deleterious effect on his physical, mental or social well-being. Four types of environment are normally involved: domestic, community, sanitary, occupational. In addition, a special type of environment is created during the process of major development schemes when all of these aspects are involved, usually with increased significance and in a manner needing special handling.

The domestic environment intimately influences physical, mental and social well-being. Much of the transmission of communicable disease, and particularly those forms which play a major part in causing the excessive mortality of childhood, takes place within the house or within its immediate surroundings. Whether transmission does take place depends as much on the way in which the house and its surroundings are used as on its actual structure. The design and methods of construction of housing have a great influence on health. Though traditional forms of building may by long custom have become adapted to their purpose in the local setting, they are not always adequate, nor are some of the newer types introduced in the conditions of rapidly growing villages and towns. In such circumstances, the local authority should intervene by introducing approved standards for new housing construction. These must not, however, be too elaborate for the economic conditions of the inhabitants. Much of the improvement of the domestic environment depends also on the personal activities of the occupier and his family, and it is for this reason that work in the field of environmental health needs to be closely linked with community development and health education programmes. These two movements can perhaps between them do more than any other single measure to limit the spread of communicable disease.

The community environment consists of the town, village or settlement and its inhabitants. Towns and villages which have been long established have, like the houses of which they consist, often developed characteristics which favour the maintenance of a satisfactory community structure within them. This is, however, seldom the case in rapidly growing villages and towns, many of which have in other countries suffered not only the ravages of communicable disease, but the breakdown of community life and the substitution of an amorphous group of which the members admit responsibility to no one, with consequent deterioration of ethical and legal standards and the spread of mental distress. What is likely to happen is that the growth of population and migration in Tanganyika will lead to a rapid increase in the size of towns and villages. There is therefore a need to guard against and mitigate these possibilities, and particularly to avoid a breakdown in sanitary management such as has been reported elsewhere in Africa.[3] Precautionary measures lie in the careful planning of rapidly growing areas; the encouragement of a social structure which facilitates family and community life; and the introduction in these areas of the self-help activities of the community development movement.

The wider environment can serve as a channel or create new channels for the transmission of communicable disease or for the spread of diseases of other types—particularly those associated with the contamination of water supplies and of food supplies as a result of the unsatisfactory disposal of wastes and sewage. A further significant aspect of disease transmission in a tropical environment is the existence of insect, rodent or snail hosts of human diseases. On the other hand, tropical countries tend to be relatively free from the

[3] Selwyn-Clarke, S. *Report on a Programme for the Health Services in Ghana*, October-December, 1961.

harmful atmospheric conditions which are a major element of ill-health in industrial countries.

Every occupation exposes the worker to hazards of some kind. In primitive farming occupations they take, for the most part, the form of hardship, stress and trauma, which are difficult to define and to avoid, but even in these circumstances special risks arise. One example is that of infection with trypanosomiasis among honey collectors which, though the numbers involved are relatively small, is of great significance as it is one of the chief means by which the disease is maintained in Tanganyika. With more sophisticated techniques of cultivation, further special risks arise. One of the more important can come from the extension of irrigation. This is the risk of infection with bilharzia, of which one form is commonly serious and sometimes fatal.

The problems arising with the aggregation of labour for work on plantations or mines are already well known and, on the whole, satisfactorily handled by a combination of industrial initiative, government regulation and external technical advice. In large part they are the problems of the migration or the re-settlement of peoples and the growth of new villages. Questions of housing, general sanitation, nutrition, protection from communicable disease, and the development of social structures embodying satisfactory relationships, all have characteristics which differ from those in more stable communities. In addition, there are the problems of achieving efficiency and reliability among the work force which, consequently, needs higher standards of health than are normally attained in much of the countryside. Special problems concern only a limited number of employees, such as safety in factories and mines, and the handling of toxic materials used in agriculture, such as weed killers and insecticides. Though much attention has been directed to estates and mines, the equally pressing problems of urban industrial employment should not be forgotten; these are at present more difficult to identify and to provide for because much of this employment is on a small scale and conditions are difficult to control. In workshops, factories, offices and shops, much industry and distribution is carried out in unhygienic, cramped, ill-lit and otherwise unsatisfactory conditions which are detrimental to the health of employees.

Problems of health and welfare are important where any large labour force is aggregated, but they become particularly pressing in major new development schemes, as for instance where a large area of hitherto unused land is reclaimed and developed for the purposes of agriculture, industry, or production of hydro-electric power. This type of growth is now an important element in Tanganyika and is likely to become progressively more important. The need for special preliminary surveys of potential health hazards and for the establishment of a single authority with powers to meet them has been respected and the risks have so far been avoided. We would, however, emphasize the need for careful scrutiny of these hazards in the future, for consultation with the Ministry of Health at the earliest planning stages and continuously thereafter, and for the inclusion of adequate provision for the management of health in the organization and in the financial structure of all future schemes.

In any recommendations provision must be made for all these aspects of environmental hygiene, without their being so ambitious as to be impossible to carry out. We suggest that responsibility for environmental hygiene should eventually be firmly placed on local authorities and that every council should be required to constitute a Health Committee charged with these duties. The work of this Committee should be closely related to the community development agency so as to secure co-ordinated activities in the environmental field. The local authority must have a guide to the necessary legislative framework in the form of a set of Model Bye-laws, applicable to the small towns and rural conditions which exist in most of Tanganyika. We have studied a set of proposed rules under Section 16 of the Native Authorities' Ordinance which deal with new buildings, dilapidated buildings, sanitation, pest control, food hygiene, dangerous and offensive trades, water supplies and other matters, which might well provide a satisfactory basis. We would suggest that a section might be added to allow local authorities to initiate other schemes of hygienic improvement, such as malaria control and schistosomiasis control, subject to the approval of the schemes by representatives of the Ministry of Health.

The local authorities will need more trained staff and we propose that the first priority should be the appointment of a trained health inspector to each Area Council, and of an assistant health inspector or a trained health orderly at lower levels. Eventually, trained health inspectors will need to be appointed to as many councils as possible.

Technical supervision and advice would be the responsibility of the headquarters of the Ministry of Health, reinforced by the inclusion of a public health engineer, below which it would be represented by the organization already proposed for Health Areas (Chapter 5). Eventually, special whole-time public health officers should be appointed to work in each region and area. A public health engineer might also be appointed at regional level.

With the growth of towns and the gradual assumption of responsibility for environmental health by the councils, there will be an increase in demand for capital works such as water, drainage and sewage schemes. Such schemes should only be undertaken after approval by the central government. Technical assistance in preparing such schemes should be provided by the public health engineers. The central government should be prepared to give grants-in-aid for approved projects.

The hygiene of estates and mines employing more than a certain minimum number of people is already controlled by existing legislation and statutory regulations. These provisions are in need of revision because much of their content employs concepts of epidemiology, of disease control and of occupational hygiene, which are now outdated. Future legislation should distinguish clearly between those responsibilities which should be made obligatory for all employers whatever their circumstances, and those which particular employers should be required to undertake either because of the lack of any alternative provisions or because of the particular circumstances of a special type of employment. There should be no exception of government departments or common service organizations in respect of their responsibilities as employers. All employers should be required to take specific measures to prevent disease or injury arising out of the employments concerned. If disease or injury should occur, they should provide full treatment either directly or by arrangement with appropriate institutions until recovery is complete. Secondly, they should be required to prevent disease or injury arising from the occupation of a dwelling or the use of such facilities as water or sewage supply, which are made available for the employees.

A general requirement for environmental sanitation and maintenance of housing, together with the prevention of diseases conveyed by domestic pests, such as malaria, would thus be laid on the employer and could be amplified by regulations. This would also make the employer responsible for preventing where possible the transference of infectious disease as a result of allocating common houses or dwellings to two or more employees. Responsibility should further be laid upon the employer for preventing the transmission of epidemic diseases within working premises or living premises which are occupied on a service tenancy.

These general requirements make it necessary for employers to maintain medical facilities, particularly for injuries arising at work. The provision of further and more general medical facilities is a question which needs to be examined with care. The worker is essentially a member of the general community and as such should be able to utilize the facilities available to the public at large. Difficulty has arisen in many countries which have large estate and mining concerns by the division of the population into two groups served by separate medical facilities. It is desirable that the employee should eventually use the same facilities as the rest of the community. The function of the employer, apart from the payment of appropriate insurance premiums, should be limited to the temporary provision of services which are made necessary by the rapid growth of population in particular areas, and to special facilities developed to meet the special needs of the employment. Consequently, medical clinics may be arranged at places and times appropriate for the particular industry, and some of these services may need to be provided at a higher standard than is possible for the rest of the country in order to improve working efficiency. Employers might well be encouraged to develop these services in line with the development of the government's health services.

To carry out its responsibilities for environmental health, industry should also be encouraged to organize its services on lines comparable to those recommended for the country as a whole. Estates which are not themselves able to employ health staff should be stimulated to form groups or associations of sufficient size to maintain such staff. Inevitably, the initial target would have to be a modest one but it might eventually be possible to envisage the employment of one trained health inspector for groups of estates containing a total of about 25,000 population. Health orderlies might be employed under their supervision for groups of about 8,000 population.

Employers should be expected to make their own arrangements for technical advice and technical supervision parallel to that given at the regional level by the Regional Medical Officer of Health. Preferably this should be arranged independently of, though in close liaison with, the Ministry of Health. When the appointed officer had been approved by government he could act in relation to industry in the same capacity as the Regional Medical Officer of Health acts in relation to the general community. These industries could then be removed from the immediate responsibility of the latter. Should it not be possible for industry to make arrangements of this kind, it might be necessary for the government to appoint the appropriate staff, charging the cost to the industries concerned.

The small urban businesses and industries which are now such a major source of bad environmental conditions are at present the responsibility of the Medical Officer of Health of the city or town concerned. It is important that progress should be made as soon as possible towards the establishment of a factory inspectorate with responsibility for all factories and workshops under a proper legislative framework.

The steps proposed are in accordance with the recommendations made by the Second and Third Sessions of the WHO Expert Committee on Environmental Sanitation. They are complementary to those made by the Ninth Session of the WHO Expert Committee on Malaria in relation to the preliminary arrangements for malaria eradication. If progress is made on these lines, the stage will be set for the development of major schemes for the control or eradication of specific diseases such as malaria. It is only when this stage is reached, and major schemes are organized, that satisfactory environmental health services will have been developed.

9 Recruitment, Training and the Problems of the Transition

The plans we have now put forward envisage the gradual development of health areas with hospitals, headquarters staff, health centres and health clinics and a health inspectorate attached to local authorities, each manned by a full complement of trained staff. Each area will need to be organized as an entity, and the different parts kept closely in balance as regards the various grades and categories of staff as well as in physical resources. We have emphasized repeatedly the importance we attach to the quality of the staff who will have to operate the new system if our recommendations are accepted. Now that we have set out our proposals for the different sections of the health services, we must discuss the recruitment and training of staff. This involves considering the problems which will face the services during the transitional phase in the next few years while additional staff are being trained.

We have arranged this Report in a way which is intended to make it easier for the reader to follow. Our proposals did not, however, evolve in the order in which they are presented. For example, we did not settle hospital and health unit establishments and then decide how many of them could be afforded. Nor did we start by determining the numbers of health units and then settle staff establishments on the basis of what could be spent. There have been several drafts and many plans for each part of the services. By trial, error and discussion we arrived at numbers of units and patterns of staffing which seemed to us to preserve a correct balance of different levels of skill, which would not make excessive demands on educated personnel, and which could be financed within the budgetary limits set in Chapter 4. In attempting to keep all these factors in balance we aimed, above all, to produce a plan for a developing national health service which would not only make sense medically but would meet the needs of Tanganyika.

In terms of cost, the bulk of the additional expenditure on staff is scheduled to be spent on four main categories: medical practitioners, medical aids (formerly rural medical aids), nurses and maternity aids. Over the next twenty years, we envisage that the number of medical practitioners working in the government and associated voluntary services will increase from about 250 to about 750; the number of medical aids from about 400 to about 2,000; and the number of trained nurses from about 1,500 to 2,250. In addition, our proposals require the recruitment and training of about 2,000 women for the new grade of maternity aid.

Quantitatively, these are the largest requirements called for by our recommendations. For this reason, much of this chapter is devoted to the problems of recruiting and training these categories of staff. We would, however, stress that other categories, though less numerous, are no less important for the execution of our proposals. Thus, we have placed a great emphasis on the need for adequate diagnostic services in the area hospitals. This means that many more laboratory and radiography technicians and assistants, pharmacy assistants, and other staff must be trained for these tasks. There are, for example, only about fifty laboratory assistants in the whole country and this number has remained about the same for eight years. A substantial increase is long overdue. There need to be many more dental assistants if the most urgent dental claims of the population are to be met. There need also to be changes in all the main training programmes to take account of the emphasis on preventive and social medicine that we propose and to enable the mentally ill to be cared for much closer to their homes. The review of training programmes in this chapter does not attempt to be exhaustive. The categories which we select for discussion are those which are quantitatively most important and those for which we are recommending major changes.

Medical Practitioners and their Auxiliaries

No category of staff has caused us greater difficulty in arriving at realistic conclusions than that of medical practitioner. At the present, there are five different grades of personnel in the government service who provide (or who attempt to provide) diagnosis and treatment: medical officers, assistant medical officers, medical assistants, rural medical aids and tribal dressers. Our plan envisages that in the long run there will be only two—medical practitioners and medical aids— and that the number in the former grade should be adequate to supervise very closely the work of the latter.

At the end of 1961, although there were 549 names on the medical register, only about 400 were thought to be resident and practising in the country; and of thirty-one licensed assistant medical officers, only about twenty were practising. About 180 of the medical practitioners are in private practice. The great majority of the medical staff come from abroad. In the government service, many of the medical staff come from the United Kingdom and Eire. In 1960, in the voluntary agencies, there were thirty-five doctors from the British Commonwealth, thirty-nine from other countries in Europe (Germany eighteen) and twenty-one from the U.S.A. Most of the private practitioners are Indian and most of them were trained in India. In the country as a whole there were in 1961 only seventeen African doctors.

At the end of 1961 there were 402 medical assistants on the register, though less than 300 were thought to be still working as medical assistants. There were 189 in central government service, about thirty-four working for local authorities and sixty for voluntary agencies. Some have recently been given special courses for six months to see whether they could be promoted to the grade of Assistant Medical Officer. Of the first class of twenty, eleven passed and two were referred. No more medical assistants are now to be trained. The government has recently decided to take this step because of changes in the educational system. In future, boys who enter secondary school will be expected to complete the four-year course and emerge at Standard XII with a School Certificate or General Certificate of Education at the 'O' level. It is unlikely, therefore, that there will be many boys leaving school with Standard X education from whom the grade of medical assistant has been recruited in the past. There are at present forty-eight in training. It is hoped that these additions to the grade will counter-balance retirements over the next few years so that the total number of medical assistants will remain constant for a period.

It is very hard to estimate how many of the present medical practitioners will be available for employment in the government and associated voluntary services under the next few years. Many of the existing expatriate staff are entitled to benefits under the Secretary of State's compensation scheme and may not wish to stay for many more years; some will soon be due to retire for reasons of age. Over the past year or two it has so far been possible to recruit medical staff to take the place of expatriates who have left the service. We hope that arrangements can be developed which will make it easier for practitioners from the United Kingdom to spend several years in Tanganyika's government service without prejudicing their opportunities in the National Health Service.[1] We hope also that the voluntary agencies will continue to bring medical staff to Tanganyika. Nevertheless, there is a danger of the position getting worse before it starts to get better. And this could be accentuated if practitioners leave the organized services for private practice. Even if foreign doctors do become available in the numbers required, and they can be afforded, we do not for one moment imagine that the government would wish to continue for more years than is essential with a staff of doctors recruited abroad. Nor do we ourselves think that many such

---

[1] Strong recommendations for this are put forward in the Porritt Report, *Medical Aid to the Developing Countries*, a Report by a Working Party for the Department of Technical Co-operation, London, 1962. Arrangements for the continuation of superannuation of doctors, dentists and nurses leaving employment in the U.K. National Health Service for employment in the Tanganyika Medical Service are described in the U.K. Ministry of Health circular H.M. (62) 4, 1962.

doctors will, in the future, be either willing or able to provide the kind of continuous service that is needed in the rural areas.

Simply from the point of view of staffing the services, more Tanganyikans must be recruited and trained for medical work. Courses of medical education of the type which are available at Makerere or in the United Kingdom are only open to those who have reached Standard XIV and obtained an Overseas Higher School Certificate or General Certificate of Education at 'A' level or the equivalent. The total number of Tanganyikans gaining such certificates in 1961 was 108. In the United Kingdom only about 4% of young people with this educational standard subsequently study medicine. The proportion could be higher in Tanganyika, but this might be at the expense of the many other occupations which desperately require graduates—particularly teaching, engineering, the legal profession and the higher levels of administration. We would think it economically unwise for an unduly large proportion of Tanganyika's best educated young people to enter medicine. In 1964, the number of persons expected to attain Higher School Certificate is 480. More distant forecasts are not available, but it seems clear that the numbers who can be spared to enter graduate courses in medicine, whether at Makerere or elsewhere, will remain low for quite a number of years.

At present, there are about a hundred Tanganyikan students studying medicine and surgery in other countries who are expected to return in the years 1963-67 (thirty-nine are studying pre-medical subjects).[2] Some will not qualify, and of those who do, not all will return. If as high an average as twenty entrants to medical school could be achieved over the five years 1963-67 inclusive, and if all these students and all the students already studying medicine were to pass their examinations and return to Tanganyika, only about 200 newly-trained practitioners would emerge during the next ten years. This is probably about the maximum number of nationals who should be spared to take this training. If it

---

[2] *List of Post-Secondary Students Studying Outside the Country and at University College, Dar es Salaam, 1961/62*, Dar es Salaam, 1962.

were assumed that the number of foreign practitioners working in the country were to remain approximately the same
for the next ten years, the addition of these 200 newly-
trained practitioners would increase the total number of
practitioners in the country to about 600. This would increase the ratio of doctors to the population, allowing for an
increase in the latter to 11·5 million, from 1 : 22,000 to about
1 : 19,000. This would still be a long way short of the WHO
recommended minimum ratio for 1970 of 1 : 10,000. Moreover, the present distribution of doctors is heavily weighted
in favour of the towns. We have described in Chapter 2 the
concentration of both private and central government practitioners in regional and district centres. In 1961, forty-five
doctors employed by the central government and sixty-six
doctors in private practice were resident in Dar es Salaam
—more than a quarter of the country's total strength of doctors. In Dar es Salaam there is at present one doctor for
1,200 people, while in the rest of the country the ratio is
1 : 31,000.

The assumptions we have made about future entrants to
medical schools and the maintenance of foreign staff at the
present level of numbers may well be regarded as unduly
optimistic. If, for example, there was a sharp fall in the number of foreign doctors and only (say) a modest fall in the
number of practising medical assistants there could be fewer
'practitioners' per head of the population ten years hence.

The prospect for the seventies is more encouraging. If the
extension and development of education in Tanganyika continues at the rapid rate of recent years, we think it possible
that by the early 1970's the number of persons obtaining
an Overseas Higher School Certificate or its equivalent each
year could run into thousands. It might then be feasible,
without unduly limiting entrants to other occupations, for
the number of entrants to medical schools to reach as high
a figure as a hundred per year. Indeed, by the middle 1970s
a limit might have to be imposed, not for reasons of denud-
ing other occupations but because of the extremely
high costs of paying for medical education, whether provided in East Africa or elsewhere. Even so, our target at the

end of twenty years of 750 practitioners in the organized services could well be achieved or even surpassed. But these new practitioners will not, however, have emerged in substantial numbers until the middle seventies. This would mean that the development of a national health service—particularly in the rural areas—could not make much progress for a good many years. While the buildings, certain other categories of staff, the equipment and the funds to develop the new services might all be available, progress would be held up because of the shortage of medical practitioners.

After making this analysis, we foresaw the possibility of many of our recommendations being postponed for a long time or shelved. The problem of medical staff for the organized services during the next ten years or so became quite crucial. And we had to bear in mind the possibilities that the rate of return of expatriates might be disastrously heavy; that recruitment from abroad during the next ten years would become more difficult; and that substantial numbers of practitioners might leave the organized services for private practice.

We came to the conclusion that, to solve the problem of the transition, we had to choose between two alternatives. Both of them, however, we would emphasize, depend upon a rapid and large-scale expansion in the number of trained medical aids—a question we discuss in detail later. The first alternative was to plan in the hope of extensive recruitment from abroad—probably unjustified optimism in view of the growing shortage of doctors in the United Kingdom, the United States, and other Western countries. The second alternative was to introduce and train in Tanganyika a new category of medical practitioner who would enter medical training earlier—at the School Certificate or 'O' level instead of Higher School Certificate or 'A' level of education—and emerge earlier.

We chose the latter course. In doing so, we were finally moved by another and more fundamental reason : the need for Tanganyikan doctors, trained to a high standard, trained to meet the health needs of Tanganyika, equipped with a philosophy of preventive medicine, and qualified to assume the roles of leader, teacher and clinician in the health centre team.

In deciding, therefore, to devise a course of training for students entering from Standard XII we noted that, in 1961 there were 531 Tanganyikans who obtained School Certificate, but that, by 1964, the number is expected to rise to over 5,000. There will, therefore, be no difficulty during the next few years in recruiting twenty-five or even fifty students a year for this course in medicine. We discuss in the next chapter the administrative requirements which we regard as essential and urgent if this new training programme is to become a reality.

In designing the curriculum for this course we have borne in mind that about one-third of all the practitioners needed for the full development of our plan will be working in the health centres. Among the newly-qualified practitioners the proportion will, of course, be much higher. This will mean that many will be living in rural areas, without the advantages and disadvantages of the towns, and working with minimal hospital facilities and specialist help. The need for doctors outside the hospital service in the rural areas is in no way unique to Tanganyika, but the contrast between rural life and town life is much greater than in many other countries. It is, therefore, particularly important that practitioners under training do not lose contact with their communities or become so sophisticated that they, or their wives, are no longer content to live and work in a rural setting. The essence of a doctor's calling anywhere in the world comes as much from the knowledge of those whom he serves as from his technical accomplishments.

The proposed new course will be open to applicants who have passed School Certificate or the General Certificate of Education at the 'O' level in the appropriate science subjects. While they will have had two years less general education than is required for University entrance, they will have had two years more education than medical assistants have had in the past. In the last two years at school they will have studied biology, chemistry and physics and their knowledge of the English language will have become more extensive. They can thus absorb a course which makes greater intellectual demands. It is proposed, therefore, that the course should last for four years and should be followed by a two-year pre-registration period during which the practitioner would be working and earning. This period would be spent in approved appointments where he could advance his training under supervision.

Since we first discussed with members of the government a draft curriculum on these lines, a WHO study group have reported on *Internationally Acceptable Minimum Standards of Medical Education.*[3] This study lends support to the concept of a four-year medical training programme based on School Certificate entry, and provides many valuable suggestions and recommendations with which we are in broad agreement.

The curriculum which we recommend corresponds in breadth to that of a Makerere-trained practitioner. Although our shorter curriculum will take students less deeply into some subjects, it lays greater emphasis on the needs of a rural practitioner.[4] It is intended that the acquisition of theoretical and clinical knowledge in hospital should be liberally supplemented with practical field experience.

We have considered the question of the status of these new Tanganyikan practitioners in relation to those trained at Makerere and overseas. This is a matter which affects East Africa as a whole, and will no doubt be discussed by the new Council for Medical and Health Education in East Africa which we understand is being set up jointly by the University of East Africa and the Ministries of Health for the four countries concerned.

At present, the registration and licensing of medical practitioners in Tanganyika is governed by the Medical Practitioners and Dentists Ordinance, 1959. This established the Medical Council of Tanganyika with the Director of Medical Services as Chairman and the Solicitor-General and not less than five other medical practitioners appointed

---

[3] Technical Report No. 239, Geneva, 1962.
[4] A general outline of the curriculum is given in Appendix C.

by the Minister as members. Among the functions of the Council are the maintenance of a register of fully-trained medical and dental practitioners, and the licensing of other specified persons thought fit to act as medical practitioners. By setting standards for admission to the register and by disciplinary action which may lead to removal of a practitioner's name, it is intended to protect both the public and the profession from unqualified persons and undesirable ethical practices.

The new Tanganyika-trained medical practitioners could (a) be placed on the Medical Practitioners' Register, (b) be licensed by the Medical Council, or (c) be placed on a separate register of their own. We ourselves would prefer to see a single register for all medical practitioners whether trained in Tanganyika or elsewhere. The entry standard, curriculum and pre-registration requirements for the new programme are above those recommended by the WHO Study Group. The Tanganyika-trained medical practitioner would be responsible, primarily in a health centre but also in area hospitals, for diagnosing and treating patients without direct supervision.

We intend that he should be regarded as 'doctor' by the nursing and technical staff and as a full professional colleague by practitioners trained at Makerere, in the United Kingdom and elsewhere. He will undoubtedly be so regarded, after six years of medical training, by all his patients. He should therefore be legally recognized as an unsupervised practitioner, and be given the privileges and be made subject to the disciplines of the medical profession. Membership of a common register does not necessarily imply a uniform degree of knowledge, skill or performance.

We have said that our proposed new course is better suited to the needs of the country. Its main emphasis is on the training of a general practitioner for rural services. The course at Makerere is more influenced by the curricula of the United Kingdom medical schools and this has advantages of a different kind which cannot be ignored. The Makerere course is generally recognized as the basis for formal postgraduate study.

We would emphasize that the new course is not intended to replace but to complement the work of the Makerere School. In terms of their recognition by the community, these new practitioners will be regarded as equal members of a profession, but different in the contribution they will make to the health needs of Tanganyika.

We recommend that the proposed new course should start in 1963 with twenty-five students and that the annual entry should be increased to fifty as soon as the facilities can be expanded. These must, however, be planned now and developed on a permanent basis. The decision about further expansion, perhaps on a two shift basis for a limited number of years, should be taken in conjunction with the new Council for Medical and Health Education in East Africa, after a review has been made of the training facilities available and of the number of students obtaining the ordinary and advanced certificates of education.

The first of the new practitioners will not, however, emerge until 1967 and they will not complete their pre-registration experience until 1969. Thus, while the creation of the new course will certainly advance by some five years the improvement in the supply of practitioners, and will produce practitioners who are better trained for the work they will have to do, it cannot improve the position to any extent until the end of the 1960s. The demand for better services will not conveniently await the supply of practitioners equipped to provide them. For many years now Tanganyika has witnessed a continuous and growing demand for more medical attention; something must be done immediately to improve the availability and quality of rural medical services—the most neglected sector among the organized services.

During this critical transition period of the 1960s a number of measures will have to be taken. Our proposals to meet this emergency situation may be summarized under four heads:

1. The most economical and efficient use of professionally trained staff in the organized services. We have already suggested a number of ways in which this might be achieved.

2. The recruitment of doctors from overseas by the Ministry of Health, the voluntary agencies and industrial concerns. Our recommendations for the reorganization of grant-aid considered as a whole will, we hope, encourage the voluntary agencies to improve the medical staffing of their hospitals.

3. Radical measures to expand as quickly as possible the supply of trained medical aids. We outline our proposals under this heading and also for maternity aids and other auxiliary grades later in this chapter.

4. Measures which aim both at providing the government with better information on a yearly basis about the medical manpower situation and at introducing some element of control over the distribution of medical practitioners.

As regards the last proposal, we have already drawn attention to the fact that in recent years the increase in the total number of registered practitioners in the organized services has barely kept pace with the increase in population, let alone with the much steeper rise in demand for medical attention. Moreover, there has been a relative loss in the organized health service sector and a substantial gain in the private sector. About three-quarters of these private practitioners work in the five largest towns. While this urban doctor:population ratio is not high by international standards, we have had to consider the possibility that during the next seven years or so there could be a further substantial rise in this concentrated private sector to the detriment of the already neglected rural areas. We were enjoined, in our terms of reference, to consider how 'to ensure maximum even coverage'. While we do not think it desirable to aim in the immediate future—even if it were possible (which it is not)—to achieve 'even coverage', nevertheless we are impelled to make certain limited proposals to prevent matters getting worse.

We therefore recommend that statutory powers be obtained to require all new entrants to the Tanganyika medical register to undertake, if called upon, a period of National Professional Service in designated institutions or appointments in the public service or approved for this purpose by the Minister. For the next ten years, or until such time as the manpower shortage is considerably reduced, we suggest a period of four years' service from the date of registration (or provisional registration in Tanganyika) with exceptions for foreign practitioners offered shorter term contract appointments in approved posts. Designated appointments would include approved voluntary agency appointments and approved training, educational and research work. We would expect this recommendation, if accepted, to be applied with due regard to the needs of the individuals concerned and the needs of the various branches of the Health Service, in respect of postgraduate training and experience at a vital stage in the professional careers of the practitioners.

An obligation would be laid on the Ministry of Health to see that this period of service was professionally fruitful and rewarding. Opportunities should be given in different posts for a wide variety of experience, and every regard should be had to the needs and abilities of the individual practitioner.

We also recommend that the Register of Medical Practitioners, and the registers of other categories of trained staff, be kept up to date by a system of annual renewal. All those on these registers would be required to make an annual return of such information that would enable the Ministry of Health to maintain a close and continuous watch on the manpower situation and the pattern of practice in all areas of the country.

As a further step during the emergency situation, we consider that the Minister should have powers to designate certain areas of the country as 'closed' to new medical practitioners. In these areas in which there is already a relatively high doctor : population ratio practitioners should not be allowed to establish practices without permission. We hope that the Minister in designating areas and fixing permitted ratios would seek the co-operation and advice of representatives of the profession.

If this recommendation were implemented, however, the existing private practitioners in areas to be 'closed' would be placed in a privileged position; the government would, so to speak, have granted them monopoly powers to practise privately in the more prosperous areas of the country. It could be argued, therefore, that during the emergency period of medical manpower shortage and in view of the monopoly created, these practitioners might be required to make some financial contribution or to render service in an appropriate professional capacity. In discussing these issues, some members of the Survey Committee held the view that the government should call upon these practitioners to make a financial contribution. Other members of the Committee, however, felt that such a recommendation was not justified. It was agreed to record this one instance in which the Committee did not reach a unanimous decision on the issues before them.

Medical Aids

At present, there are rather more than 400 medical aids employed, of whom 368 are working for local authorities, twenty-six for the central government, and a small number for the voluntary agencies. This number is far from sufficient to staff all the existing dispensaries. In 1961 about half the dispensaries were staffed by tribal dressers. The main reason for this has been not so much the lack of training facilities for medical aids but the reluctance of some local authorities to pay the extra salaries needed to engage trained staff. In recent years the training intake at the government centres has varied between twenty and forty a year. The training facilities at Mwanza and Bukoba together could admit a total of eighty students each year. This training lasts for two years and there has been no shortage of applicants with Standard VIII education which is required. Indeed, over 500 recently applied for the forty places made available. Many applicants take jobs as hospital orderlies while hoping to be offered a place at the training school.

We recommend that the full complement of eighty students should be admitted as soon as possible. Immediate steps should also be taken to develop further training facilities in other parts of Tanganyika so that the number admitted for training is temporarily increased to a total of at least 200 per year. The facilities required are not elaborate and could be developed at any 'B' hospital with adjacent health centres, providing that staff with the prime function of teaching were made available. We have no major criticisms to make of the syllabus, which we regard as admirable for its purpose. We would, however, suggest that after the immediate shortage has been overcome the possibility should be considered of a further year being spent in an 'approved' post before registration. We also think it desirable that a newly-trained medical aid should work for a time at a health centre under supervision before he starts work in a health clinic on his own.

Within the next three years a start should be made with 'post-qualification' training programmes for medical aids, either along the lines of the up-grading courses run for them at Ifakara or in special in-service training posts at teaching health centres. Such training given to selected aids would fit them for posts as senior medical aids in health centres where they would have to take charge when the practitioner was absent. The further training of medical aids for special duties in hospitals is probably best done in the hospitals requiring their services.

Our proposed crash programme for the training of medical aids should bring some relief to medical staff and medical assistants who are at present working under heavy pressure. We hope that some of these medical aids will be employed in hospital casualty departments as an interim measure before health area facilities are organized and staffed to operate under the new plan. We hope also that sufficient staff will be available for health clinics so that by 1970 no dispensary, in the charge of tribal dresser, will remain in Tanganyika.

Our plan for the next twenty years envisages a need for an eventual total of about 2,000 medical aids to staff the government and associated voluntary agency services: about 1,000 practising in health clinics, 600 practising in health centres (of which 200 should be senior medical aids) and 150 who have taken further training for work in class

'B' hospitals. If there are few retirements over the next fifteen years, training facilities for 200 per year would ultimately produce more aids than are required. In such circumstances there would be no difficulty in reducing training facilities in the middle 1970s. By that time a higher educational standard might be demanded on entry to the course.

Nursing and Related Services
As we have already stated, our plan envisages an increase from about 1,500 nurses[5] working in government and voluntary agency services at the end of 1960 to about 2,250 in 1980. The great majority of the present trained nursing staff are on Part B of the register, having entered nursing with Standard VIII education and been trained for three years. The smaller number who are on Part A of the register include those who have received two years' further training in the United Kingdom (this period has recently been reduced to one year for girls trained at the new Princess Margaret School); those who, after Part B registration, have attended a new special one-year course held in Dar es Salaam; and those nurses trained wholly overseas. Until recently, most of the posts of matron and sister were held by expatriates. Many of the latter have now left Tanganyika and their places have been taken by Tanganyikans.

In addition to the hospital nursing grades, there are locally trained midwives. The course normally lasts for two years but trained nurses can take it in one year. Until recently there was also a course of training for health nurses which was introduced in 1952. It was a practical two-year course orientated towards home care, health education and preventive work. As explained in Chapter 2, these courses

---

[5] The Government establishment for trained nursing and midwifery staff in 1962, excluding tutorial and health visiting posts, was 218 Part A and 767 Part B. The number of trained nursing and midwifery staff working in the voluntary hospitals was approximately 400 at the end of 1960. It may, therefore, be estimated that there are approximately 1,500 trained nurses and midwives currently working in the government and voluntary hospitals. At the end of 1961, there were 1,999 names on the nursing register and 905 on the midwives register. Some persons were entered on both registers and an unknown number had retired—at least temporarily.

have now been replaced by one combined nurse/midwife course available to girls or boys with Standard VIII education, which lasts for three years and includes a considerable amount of public health nursing. This training can be taken at the one government school (at the Princess Margaret Hospital) or at any of the fourteen schools run by the voluntary agencies. Those who complete the course have their names entered on Part B of the register. A fourth year of training will be held only at the Princess Margaret Nursing Training School and be available for selected applicants from Part B training schools. Six months of this period will be spent in more advanced hospital nursing. In the case of girls, the other six months will be devoted to midwifery. Male nurses will be given training in 'special subjects' such as operating theatre technique, mental nursing, tuberculosis nursing, leprosy nursing and hospital administration.

In recent years, the number of nurses completing their training has been increasing rapidly and there has been some indication of unemployment. Over the next three years, the number of nurses expected to complete the basic course will be around 200 a year. The majority are being trained by the voluntary agencies: some of these training hospitals are, however, too small to be able to offer a full range of experience. By 1958, the government had training facilities for fifty female and fifty male nurses per year, but reduced the intake to about one-half of that number for financial reasons. It is difficult to say how much the responsibilities of marriage and child-rearing will reduce the services given by trained nurses, but it seems probable, from an analysis of the available statistics, that an increase of trained nurses from 1,500 to 2,250 by 1980 should present no problem. Indeed, if all training facilities were used (irrespective of their quality), and if a second government training school were opened when the new hospital at Mwanza is completed, more nurses would be trained than the services could afford to employ. It will be important, therefore, that the position should be reviewed periodically. It is for this reason we have earlier recommended that the register of nurses be kept up to date annually. Much will depend on the rate at which trained nurses give up work on account of marriage and family responsibilities. Should this not be a material factor, and if a trend develops towards unemployment in the profession this would be a favourable opportunity to raise the educational standard on entry and to concentrate training on those few schools which can provide a wide range of experience and employ adequate tutorial staff.

Our proposals for health units envisaged the employment in these services of about 2,000 'maternity aids'. This is a new grade we recommend, for which training should be specially developed. What we have in mind is a course on the lines of the recently abandoned training for health nurses but with a more substantial emphasis on midwifery. We feel that in the present circumstances there is a distinct advantage in combining in one person responsibilities for supervision of the confinement and for advice on the care of infants. In addition to the detection of abnormalities before confinement, these maternity aids should concentrate much of their efforts on education in child care. They should be trained to regard the supervision of the confinement not as the principal or only service they render, but as the means by which they gain the confidence of mothers for their primary work of health education.

In her own field the maternity aid must possess skills which are comparable and complementary to those of the medical aid with whom she will need to work in close partnership. We suggest that the training should last for two years and that applicants should be required to have Standard VIII education. Training should be based on 'B' hospitals and their associated health units. Indeed, it would seem desirable for the training to be conducted at the same places where training for medical aids is being given, so that joint instruction can be arranged in the general field of public health and education. We hope that many practising maternity aids will be older, and married women, as this would contribute to their influence in the local community and their understanding of the problems of motherhood. Every encouragement should therefore be given to married women to apply for training, and for those who are trained to remain in practice after marriage.

Health Inspectors
The health inspectorate consists of health inspectors who have been trained and recruited overseas, assistant health inspectors who are required to have Standard X education and are given three years' training, health orderlies who, until 1958, were required to have Standard VI education and were given a one-year training, and sanitary inspectors. Since 1958, health orderlies have been trained region-ally and there has been, in consequence, considerable variation in standards. Sanitary inspectors, who are no lon-ger trained, had more specialized but less formal instruction than health orderlies.

While most of the health inspectors and assistant health inspectors have been employed by the central government, they have been seconded to work for local authorities mainly in the urban areas. The value of their services has not always been appreciated and we found the morale of the inspectorate at a low ebb : half the foreign staff had retired or given notice. The limited success of the health inspectorate service over the years in winning public sup-port and co-operation does not surprise us. It is not easy for overseas trained staff to impose what may be regarded as alien standards of public health conduct. Nevertheless, the problems of environmental health—particularly in the rural areas—need much greater emphasis if there is to be any real progress in raising standards of community health. In the future we would like to see, in all training programmes, more prominence given to the environmental health of small towns and villages.

We do not believe, however, that real advances will come about until the service is directed at the local level by in-spectors who are locally recruited and trained in East Africa. We are, therefore, glad to hear that steps are being taken to up-grade existing assistant health inspectors to the grade of full inspector. We also welcome the plan for a new three-year training programme for health inspectors to be run by the Princess Margaret Training School in conjunction with the Technical College in Dar es Salaam and the City Council. It is to be based on an intake at School Certificate level, and it is confidently hoped that it will be recognized for the Royal Society Health Certificate in Public Health Inspection for General Overseas Appointments. It is intended that eight or ten students should commence study early in 1963. In the long run, however, we would like to see the development of regular courses of this kind organized to serve all the countries of East Africa. The provision of relatively small training needs in such categories can be met much more efficiently and economically by international co-operation of this kind.

As regards the auxiliary grades in the public health field (health orderlies and sanitary inspectors) we recommend that there should be some systematization of training arrangements. While courses might still be conducted at regional level under the Regional Health Inspector, we recommend that conditions should be laid down for the standard of entry and the duration of the course. Most of the training should be conducted on the job directly under the supervision of a health inspector but a national examination should be introduced. Candidates should be expected to have an elementary knowledge of the appropriate legislation and an understanding of the health aspects of water and food supply, the disposal of waste and refuse, and the control of mosquitoes and vermin.

The Mental Health Services

The inclusion of a certain amount of study of mental nursing as one of the options in the fourth year of the nursing course will help to produce male nurses to staff the psychiatric units of general hospitals and to work in health centres. We would like to see the option of six months' mental nursing also made available for women. It is hoped that nurses who have taken this option will then be able to nurse acute mental patients for short spells or less acute patients for longer periods in the area health services. Such training will not, however, be adequate for nurses who are going to work in the mental hospitals at Dodoma and the new proposed hospital at Dar es Salaam. We have mentioned in Chapter 6 that sixteen nurses are at present undergoing a two-year training in mental nursing in the United Kingdom. On their return it should be possible with their help to arrange for a special course of training in mental nursing in Tanganyika. Although the numbers required are relatively small, this is an urgent need.

We also recommended in earlier chapters the introduction of a grade of mental welfare assistant to help with the social work needs and resettlement of mental patients. We have suggested that such an assistant might be appointed to each area headquarters and that a number of selected students should be sent to the United Kingdom for training. Ideally, however, we would like to see a training course developed for these workers on an East African basis. As we have very recently learnt of the establishment of a course in social work at Makerere, we think that this might be the most suitable place for mental welfare assistants to be trained. In our view, this course should last for two years, it should combine both theoretical and practical work, and should include some element of education in the skills and methods of casework and group work. Applicants should be required to have Standard XII education.

Health Administration Staff

On several occasions in our Report we have drawn attention to the lack of lay administrative staff and the large burden of such work which consequently falls upon medical practitioners, distracting them from the duties for which they are trained. The shortage of experienced administrators in Tanganyika extends far beyond the health services and we are not suggesting that the requirements of these services ought to have been met out of turn. The need is now, however, an urgent one, and a number of measures should be taken quickly. With the development of the educational system it should be possible to select a number of young men with appropriate education, and provide them with in-service training to act as lay health administrators in the hospitals and in area, regional and central headquarters. Some such staff might be sent overseas for special advanced training, as recommended in the report *Medical Aid to the Developing Countries.*[6]

Meanwhile, selected clerical or other staff might be given in-service training and offered courses at the Technical College, the new Institute of Public Administration or the Princess Margaret Training College. The establishment of twelve posts of hospital administrative assistant at the level of Ex 2 and Ex 3 is to be welcomed, and six have so far been promoted from the clerical staff. The possibility of engaging a supernumerary hospital administrator from the United Kingdom for one to two years to help with the organization of in-service training might well be considered.

A Health Unit Training School

To this point we have considered separately and in turn certain major categories of staff needed for the reorganization and development of the health services. But we do intend that the health unit system proposed should be something more than the sum total of the efforts of separately trained individuals working in the same area. We are, in fact, asking for team work and co-operation of a high order. Inevitably, much will depend on the individuals concerned; how they respond to one another; and how far they apply in practice a common approach to health problems which will, we hope, have been emphasized in all their training programmes. But, in so far as team work can be taught by practice and example, we suggest that this should be done.

Before new health units start to operate in a newly designated health area we regard it as essential for the senior members of each new health unit team to attend a residential course in health centre management at a model centre maintained for this purpose. Each member of the team by study in the classroom and observation in the centre must learn his or her role and exactly how it relates to that of others. At this stage, details of administration should be taught and staff should learn how to plan their daily pro-

---

[6] *op. cit.*

grammes. They should be attached to the model centre as supernumeraries but before they have left they must be made to run the centre themselves under supervision. Thus, we hope that every team will go to its work in a new health area with the highest morale and imbued with the highest standards of conduct. We hope too that the model centre will be constantly studying new methods of management, testing new administrative procedures, and working out new ways of co-operating with community development, agricultural, local government and other local agencies. We would hope to see the model centre acting in every sense as the staff college of the local health services.

10 Regional and Central Services

We have outlined in earlier chapters a plan for the health services which we wish to see developed on a national scale. We have indicated that we would like the role of the voluntary agencies to be gradually confined to the provision of hospitals, and the role of local government to be restricted to the provision of environmental health services. Thus, the central government would itself provide all the local *personal* health services outside hospital as well as being responsible for a large part of the hospital and specialist services; it would also give technical supervision to the work of the local authorities and, in conjunction with the voluntary agencies, plan the development of the hospital services as a whole.[1] In this chapter we consider the changes in the central and regional organization of the health department needed to implement these proposals.

At present the department operates through nine regional officers and the Medical Superintendent of the Dar es Salaam hospitals. Our plan envisages the development of forty health areas, thirty-seven of them served by 'B' hospitals (twenty-two areas sharing a hospital and fifteen having one to themselves) and three of them (Dar es Salaam, Mwanza and a third possibly in the north of the country) served by 'A' hospitals. As and when more resources become available, additional areas can be designated. Eventually it might be desirable to adjust the boundaries and numbers of health areas to those of district councils. At the time of preparing

[1] See Organizational Chart, Appendix A.

this Report, the long-term future of local government and of the regional administration had not been clarified. Decisions in this field could provide reasons for modifying certain details of our plan. But whatever the exact number of health areas, it seems to us essential to preserve and strengthen a system of regional organization. The health areas will be too numerous, and many of them geographically too remote, to have direct links with the central department.

The Regional Organization

Regional medical officers will have three principal responsibilities. The first will be to supervise and co-ordinate the work of the hospitals in the region. This will involve the development of close relationships with the voluntary agencies operating 'B' hospitals in the region. While questions of general policy concerning the voluntary agencies will be settled by discussion between the Voluntary Agency Planning Committee and the Ministry, it is desirable that matters of day-to-day administration, including the interpretation of grant regulations, should be channelled through the regional office. We hope it will be rare for agreement on such matters not to be reached at regional level. At present there seems to us to be too much of a tendency for voluntary agencies to raise at headquarters—particularly at Ministerial or Chief Medical Officer level—matters which could and should be settled locally.

In areas where the area hospital is a voluntary hospital the regional medical officer, or his representative, will have a seat on the hospital board. Where the area hospital is a government hospital, the medical superintendent will be responsible to the regional medical officer for the running of his hospital. We recommend, however, that Area Hospital Advisory Committees should gradually be established. The regional medical officer or his deputy would take the chair and the members might include the area medical officer, one or more representatives of the local authority, and a representative of the local community development agency. All meetings of the committee would be attended by the medical superintendent, the chief nursing officer and the administrative assistant. We do not envisage such committees meeting frequently (perhaps once every three months) but we regard such a committee as a valuable means of co-ordinating the area health service, quite apart from providing local democratic representatives with opportunities to participate in the responsibilities of hospital management.

A second responsibility of regional medical officers will be the technical supervision of the work of local authorities in the field of environmental health. While there will be direct contact between the regional medical officer and individual hospitals, the channel of communication with district councils will be through the area health officer. To ensure that appropriate attention is given to matters of environmental health, we suggest that the regional medical officer should be given a deputy who is wholly engaged on stimulating action in the preventive field. It will be his task to work with and assist local authorities in the region, as well as to co-ordinate the preventive activities which different area officers are undertaking through their health units.

Thirdly, regional medical officers will be responsible through their area officers for all the work of the health units themselves. They must ensure that the crucial task of supervision is not neglected in any health area. Should difficulties arise between the health unit services and the hospital, or between any other medical services in each area, it will be the task of the regional officer to resolve them.

Apart from these functional responsibilities, certain routine matters will be channelled through the regional office —particularly the distribution of stores, systems of financial allocation and control, and statistical services. At present, some regional officers are forced to spend too much time at their desks undertaking tasks which require little or no medical knowledge. We suggest that each regional officer should be given a senior lay administrator and appropriate clerical staff as soon as the supply of people with these skills is sufficient for such allocations to be made. We believe that with the aid of better communications in the form of a radio link, where telephones do not exist, with headquarters, hospitals and area health headquarters, these administrative functions could be carried out more efficiently and economically.

Headquarters

About the distribution of work among the senior officers of the department at headquarters, we do not wish to make firm proposals. Inevitably, much must depend on the skill and abilities of those who fill these critically important posts. But, ideally, the Chief Medical Officer might find it useful to act through three deputies with separately defined functions. The first and most senior would be responsible for preventive work of every kind. Under him would come the new epidemiological division, whose functions we shall define later in this chapter, and all the other units concerned with preventive action or research. Technical advice and instructions for the organization of campaigns, demonstrations or surveys would be channelled through him to the regional organization. The second deputy would be responsible for maintaining and developing the standards of the curative services throughout the country. He would thus have responsibilities for the specialist and hospital services. The third deputy would be generally responsible for all training arrangements; for programmes undertaken in Tanganyika and for programmes which involve sending staff for training to other countries. In such matters the principal matron would come under the control of this deputy. In other matters, as chief adviser to the Chief Medical Officer on nursing affairs, she would have direct access to the latter.

The Training Schools

The recommendations which we have made in Chapter 9 involve a considerable expansion in training activities. The introduction of a course of training for medical practitioners will make much greater demands on teachers, library and laboratory facilities and on the staff of Princess Margaret Hospital. The course, moreover, raises many new problems, both professional and academic. We think it desirable, therefore, to recommend changes in the administration of the training schools to take account of these new needs and developments.

At present there are two training schools at Princess Margaret Hospital, one for nurses and midwives and the other for the assistant grades (medical assistants, dental assistants, laboratory assistants, assistant health inspectors and hospital steward assistants). There are advantages in this concerntration of training programmes in Dar es Salaam. Joint use can be made of classrooms, libraries, laboratories and hostels. A wide range of part-time teachers is available and the students have the opportunity of meeting those who will be working in closely related fields. There is, on the other hand, a very real danger that students will become too accustomed to urban life and to extensive social activities and thus lose touch with the communities from which they have come. That is one reason why we lay so much stress on practical work in the field for all who will be required to serve in rural areas. Moreover, it is important that these students should be familiar with and understand the needs and problems of those living in these areas. Provided such field work arrangements and teaching are given as much prominence as possible the concentration of the main training facilities in the capital seems unavoidable.

The training schools at present come under the control of the Medical Superintendent of the Princess Margaret Hospital. We believe that this should continue in the case of the Nurses' Training Centre in view of the major contribution to the work of the hospital which is made by the student nurses. In the case of the Training School for the other staff, however, we consider that the time has come to create a separate Board of Governors with a separate financial vote to undertake this responsibility. In addition to representatives from his department, we would recommend that the Minister of Health should appoint to this Board representatives from the Department of Education, the medical and other faculties of the University of East Africa, and the Technical College of Dar es Salaam. The Governors should appoint a full-time principal who would be responsible for all the courses for medical practitioners and for the assistant grades referred to above. These duties might be carried out by a series of 'course committees', composed of all participating full-time and some part-time teachers, of which the principal would be chairman. These course committees would also be responsible for approving posts in hospitals and health centres for pre-registration appointments. A lay bursar should also be appointed whose duty it would be to ensure that all the facilities of the school are up to the standard required for the courses. This includes residential accommodation both at the school and at the hospitals and health centres visited during training and designated for pre-registration appointments. It is essential that adequate accommodation be provided for married students and pre-registration practitioners.

One of our reasons for recommending the creation of this Board and the appointment of a full-time principal and bursar is the need for a new and imaginative approach to the teaching of preventive and social medicine in the context of Tanganyika and its problems. There is very great scope for the pioneering and development of new methods of instruction and examining; the use of visual and other aids; the production of case studies, text-books and other materials; the organization of combined theoretical and field exercises; experiments in joint discussions with students and practitioners in neighbouring disciplines, and so forth. This is undoubtedly an area of need for which aid might be sought in the form of financial help and expert advice from international agencies and education foundations.

Although the training programmes for medical aids and maternity aids should share in and benefit from developments of this kind we do not recommend that these courses should be held in Dar es Salaam. They need to be based on 'B' hospitals with adjacent health centres in other areas of Tanganyika.

An Epidemiological Division
Epidemiological services are concerned with changes in the incidence of diseases, both endemic and epidemic, with the emergence of 'new' diseases and the disappearance of others.

The study of the reasons for these changes has many aspects —social, demographic, genetic, zoological, climatic and, of course, statistical. Such study has a critical part to play in the prevention and control of epidemics of communicable disease. It should not, however, be confined to these more dramatic areas. The incidence of accidents and injuries and of all physical and mental diseases should be regularly studied.

The staff of the Ministry of Health already have considerable expertise in the sphere of communicable diseases, and have in the past made substantial contributions to knowledge in this field. The former Malaria Unit (now Epidemiological Unit) has recently expanded its activities to cover mosquito-borne diseases in general, and to undertake work in such fields as plague and bilharzia. In the special units concerned with trypanosomiasis, leprosy, tuberculosis and nutrition a considerable amount of essential information has been accumulated. Much of this work is parallel to that undertaken by the EACSO[2] Research Unit at Mwanza on filariasis and bilharzia. Other sources of information are the Medical Officers of Health, the pathology laboratory and hospital clinical records.

Information from all these sources is of the greatest value for the formulation and execution of health policies. But there are large gaps. Indeed, when we attempted a review of the health needs of Tanganyika in Chapter 3, we came to see how little systematic knowledge there was on a variety of important questions. Although data are collected concerning the work of the health services the material is not at present analysed or presented in a form from which useful conclusions can be drawn. What is needed now is to broaden the scope and improve the reliability of the information available to the Ministry. This would best be secured by establishing a central epidemiological division. Such a division must not be permanently orientated to particular sectors of the health field but charged with wide responsibilities. And it should be flexible enough to be able to concentrate its studies in relation to observed and anticipated trends.

---

[2] East African Common Services Organization.

What we are envisaging is a technical unit without any administrative functions, which will collect and analyse data from all relevant sources including those concerned with special branches of medicine (e.g. child health, mental health, ophthalmology). The unit should have access to all these sources of information on the prevalence of disease, and be equipped to give technical advice on such matters as immunization and other control measures. It should establish close relationships and exchange information with research workers in medical, sociological and related fields both in Tanganyika and at University and EACSO centres. It should recommend research programmes to the Ministry, and itself initiate and undertake independent *ad hoc* surveys whenever the need arises for more urgent or more precise information than is available from standard returns.

Such a division need not involve a large addition to the present establishment of staff nor require elaborate equipment. A trained epidemiologist should direct the division, and he should be provided with staff and equipment for a statistical section and have one or more field officers with transport to act as the nucleus of survey teams. These would be deployed for particular investigations and be augmented by trained staff drawn from the special units appropriate to the particular study or campaign being undertaken.

It might be thought that some of the special units such as the (former) Malaria Unit and the Trypanosomiasis and Leprosy Units should come under the direct administrative control of the epidemiological division. We feel that this would be a mistake. The central division should not be burdened with the administrative work which would be involved nor should its orientation be biased to particular subjects, however important these may be. The special units for their part require freedom to develop the links they have already established with other research units, the hospitals, the Ministry of Natural Resources, and with local government. It is particularly important that the trypanosomiasis service now based on Tabora should be kept in existence under specialist direction. The former Malaria Unit might well extend its activity to become a Vector-borne Diseases

Division concerned with parasitic and insect-borne disease in general, possibly incorporating the trypanosomiasis service as one of its units. While over-centralization would be a mistake, the close co-ordination of these activities should lead to some economy and provide the scientists working in these parallel and overlapping fields with a stimulus and new opportunities for collaboration.

We wish to stress the importance of establishing an epidemiology division because it could make an essential contribution to the development of the health services, particularly on the preventive side. It would be the source of authoritative information on the nation's health and the intelligence unit for the continuous conduct and evaluation of health campaigns.

Vital Statistics
The work of an epidemiological division would be of more value if improvements could be made in national vital statistics. The full development of a system for the registration and certification of births and deaths will not be practicable for many years to come. Meanwhile, such preliminary measures as are practicable should be undertaken. They are particularly needed for the continuous study of population trends.

Compulsory notification of the facts of birth and death (without certificate of the cause of death), date and identification by name (or name of parent), sex, approximate age (and possibly birth order) could be introduced initially in designated areas and extended later throughout the country. This has in fact been done on a small scale in some parts of East Africa for a number of years. A beginning of this kind in Tanganyika would prepare the way for the eventual introduction of legislation to provide for the certification of the cause of death. The operation of such a system falls outside the functions of the Ministry of Health and should be the responsibility of a Registrar-General.

In Chapter 4 we drew attention to the need for the collection of census material at more frequent intervals than ten years. We hope that much use can be made of sample and other economical methods. It is highly important—particularly for health service planning—that close and continuing study should be made of population trends.

Laboratory Services

We recommend that the present pathology laboratory service should be gradually split up into two separate agencies —one to provide a clinical diagnostic service in association with the hospitals, the other to act as a public health and forensic laboratory service. This does not necessarily imply entirely separate staff and accommodation. The public health laboratory should have the closest relations with the epidemiological division. It could also with advantage develop a nutritional laboratory section.

Nutritional Services

It is only recently that a separate unit for the study of nutrition has been established. Its activities have been very limited owing to shortage of funds, and the medical officer who set up the unit has lately accepted an appointment elsewhere. There is no doubt that the intensive study of nutritional problems has a critical part to play in health education and preventive medicine. Much more needs to be known about local food habits and taboos to form the basis for agricultural, veterinary and health education activities. The study of this subject, therefore, deserves more attention than can be given by one medical officer. We are well aware that the main difficulty is the world shortage of qualified staff. We suggest that the Ministry should give high priority to sending several staff members and at least two medical officers abroad for intensive training in nutritional survey methods so that eventually the unit's activities could be enlarged. In all its fieldwork, the unit should be in close touch with the Department of Co-operative and Community Development and the Epidemiology Division.

Nutrition, Health Education and Home Economics

It will be one of the increasingly important tasks of the Ministry of Health and its associated units to provide technical advice, teaching, demonstration materials, and specialist staff to assist all those working in these basically educational fields. They are all related in their essential purpose to change human behaviour, individual and collective, and to raise levels of living. Repeatedly, throughout this Report, we have stressed two principles: that the approach to better health must be through prevention, and that this principle should continuously inform the day-to-day functions of the health centres; secondly, that these centres, by drawing on the strengths of the local self-help and community development agencies, should become a local powerhouse of activity in communicating and demonstrating the lessons of nutrition, crop production, health education and home economics.

The particular skills of the community development movement, illustrated in such reports as Professor Belshaw's *Report on Community Development in Africa* (1956), Mr. V. L. Griffith's *An Enquiry into Community Development in Uganda* (1960) and Miss T. Spens' *Report on Home Economics in Africa* (1962), should be assisted by technical advice and aid from the Ministry of Health and its specialized units. It might, therefore, be helpful to second a medical officer from the Ministry of Health to the Ministry responsible for community development. He could assist in measures of co-ordination and provide specialist advice in the planning of health education policies, training programmes and campaigns.

The Financial Accounts
In Chapter 2 we attempted to analyse expenditure on health services according to different functional categories of expenditure. This involved a substantial amount of estimating and checking. Understandably, the present accounts have not been devised for this purpose and are intended to provide a means of financial control. We think that functional accounts have an important role to play in the formulation and application of policy and we therefore recommend that the form of accounts should be revised so that a simple functional breakdown is used both for estimates and for appro-

priations. The World Health Organization has, over recent years, undertaken considerable studies in this field and has recently devised a system of functional accounts for use in countries at all levels of development.[3] This functional breakdown might well be used by Tanganyika in its ordinary budgetary processes.

The Allocation and Posting of Staff

At present all qualified staff in the central government service are allotted their duties from headquarters. This system of 'posting' has tended to lead to very frequent changes of medical staff. In recent years these have been largely attributable to the considerable number of retirements and replacements which have been taking place. In the last chapter, we stressed the importance of practitioners getting to know well the communities in which they are working. It takes several years for a practitioner to become thoroughly familiar with the capacities of his staff, with the habits of the local community, and with at least some of the patients. Knowledge of this kind greatly enhances his effectiveness both as a leader and as a doctor. It is, therefore, highly desirable that staff changes should be kept to a minimum. Moreover, it is preferable for a practitioner to choose his place of work or to feel he has chosen it rather than to think it has been imposed upon him.

The government is in a position to control the number of vacancies in its service. It can, therefore, ensure that this number is always kept fairly close to the number of practitioners seeking appointment. We suggest that an attempt should be made to substitute a system of appointment by application for the system of posting. Vacancies would be advertised and candidates would be encouraged to apply to the region concerned which would be empowered to make the selection. We accept that such a system could result in the least attractive candidates getting the least attractive appointments and, occasionally, in vacancies going unfilled for some period. But we feel that these disadvantages are less

[3] Abel-Smith, B. *Paying for Health Services*, W H O Public Health Paper, Geneva, 1963.

than those which accompany a system of posting. We would, however, make an exception with practitioners entering the service for the first time who should be 'posted' to a succession of different posts to gain the experience they need.

11 Conclusions

We should not have written this Report in the way we have if we did not believe that what lies ahead for Tanganyika is a challenging opportunity to pioneer, develop and set standards of health care which could be an inspiration and an example for other independent nations. In our proposals for a unified health service, we have thus tried to look with Tanganyikan eyes on the needs of the Tanganyikan people. We want to draw on the strengths of the community development and self-help movement so that the improvement of health involves the people and is not just a matter of drugs, doctors and hospitals. We want to see a health service developing which will not be separate and aloof from the life of the nation but an expression and reinforcement of national unity.

These are the guiding thoughts which underlie the many detailed recommendations we have now made. They explain why at times we have shown little respect for alien institutions. They explain why we have not produced an expensive blue-print calling for large numbers of experts and specialists from overseas, chromium-plated resources and impressive equipment which cannot be afforded. These facilities are not, of course, to be scorned just because they are expensive or just because they can benefit directly only a tiny proportion of the people. Medical care is just as much a question of priorities for government as any other public good. In a situation in which the dresser and the medical aid are at present the real practitioners for the mass of the people, and less than ten shillings per head per year is likely to be available for spending on health services for many years to come, we have been forced, again and again, to choose between what is ultimately desirable and what is practicable in the immediate future.

Our first major choice was to accept the decision of the people. Spending on education will come before spending on medicine. Investment in teaching in the broadest sense will come before investment in doctoring. A better educated people will better appreciate how they themselves can prevent disease and sickness. Hence we have laid great emphasis throughout our Report on the need to develop and expand the role of preventive health care. The foundations of better health lie in childhood: we therefore wish to see the maternity and child welfare services playing an increasingly important part in the work of the health centres and clinics. The provision of medical treatment by medical auxiliaries at these units must also be seen as a means of furthering health education; of advising on and teaching the simple but supremely important principles of nutrition, germ infection and the home care of sick children. To raise standards of health among mothers and children must assuredly contribute to the raising of educational standards in general; healthier children will derive more benefit from an expanding system of education at school.

A second message that runs through our Report is the need to harness the community development and self-help movement to the work of the local health services. The health centres, with their satellite health clinics, and their links with area hospitals, should further their aim to provide good medical care by becoming local powerhouses of health education and preventive medicine. We see them acting as demonstration and group teaching centres in healthier living; consulting, advising and assisting local leaders and groups, health workers and midwives in how to work with others in raising levels of living.

Through these and other of our recommendations we believe that the pace of improvement in health standards can be quickened. More people will be reached more quickly;

more people will be asked and expected to participate actively in these local campaigns. The process will be a continuing one; health education must be a sustained and shared effort; medical care must be rooted in that continuity of attention which respects the dignity of people in contrast to the frustrations of sporadic dispensary treatment and occasional assaults on particular diseases. A permanent stage will thus be set for a sustained attack on malaria, tuberculosis and many other diseases which at present cause so much ill-health and suffering.

Malaria eradication, as the World Health Organization has declared, is not a matter of miracles suddenly imposed from without by benevolent international agencies. It can only be achieved from within by building a community health organization; on such foundations malaria can be banished. To prepare the way for technical international help, therefore, many methods must be used, not least that of community development which strives to bring about change by the willing co-operative effort of the community itself.

In deciding that we should produce a plan which would be consistent with the national objective of investing more in education and in developing agricultural and industrial resources, we settled on a broad target for the health services. We assumed that current expenditure on the organized health services could be allowed to double over the period to 1980. This should be within the capacity of the country; it should not call for a larger proportion of the national product than is spent today. It means an increase in current spending by Government and the voluntary agencies of about 4% a year. Given more generous foreign aid in cash and in kind, our plan is sufficiently flexible to allow the pace of improvement to be substantially quickened.

In accepting a limit to the size of the government's health budget, we forced ourselves to answer a number of questions. These can be simply put : how to achieve the maximum health benefit for the maximum number of people; how and in what ways to train more health workers as quickly as possible; what changes would be needed in the planning, organization and operation of the services to accomplish these aims.

The answers to these questions and, inevitably, they are detailed answers, are to be found in our long list of principal recommendations. With a limited health budget, most of them demand the planned use of scarce health resources; planning at the centre; planning at regional and district levels; planning in the disposition of the health unit system we propose, and planning in the step-by-step improvement of area health care facilities.

Tanganyika is fortunate in having at present a headquarters staff which has laid sure and sound foundations. But they cannot be built on until two major difficulties are removed. First, the central government must take over the responsibility for all the personal health services run by local government. Second, there must be unification of the services maintained by the central government and the voluntary agencies. We believe that, if certain conditions are fulfilled, this can be achieved without nationalization. Accordingly, we have put forward two alternative schemes which we hope the voluntary agencies will consider with great seriousness. In both these schemes, we have done our best to respect the religious affiliations and traditions of the agencies.

Planning, however, is not only a matter of seeing that hospitals, health centres and health clinics are built or extended in the right places and in the right proportions. It is also a matter of seeing that trained staff and the institutions in which they work do the jobs they are trained and fitted to do. We want hospitals to be hospitals and not all-purpose dispensaries. We want doctors to be doctors and not all-purpose workers. Only a unified service can ensure that specialized workers do specialized things, and that in doing so they help in the education and supervision of the work of the less specialized.

Throughout our Report we have laid great emphasis on the need for continual supervision and the raising of standards among auxiliary medical staff. Again, only a unified service can sustain these tasks and to do so must mean a better deployment of the more highly trained staff. But, with the exception of nurses, Tanganyika is desperately short of trained health workers of all categories and grades. The rural areas are by far the most impoverished; we estimate that at present there are only two to three trained doctors for every 100,000 people in the rural areas. We have therefore given the most serious attention to the problems of staffing the rural health services. In our proposals they are given high priority, for we believe that better medical care in these areas can help to limit the drift of people to the towns, and can contribute to the drive for agricultural expansion which plays a critical part in the Government's economic development plan.

While the people themselves, individually and collectively, can do much to improve their levels of health, nevertheless trained staff are required in much larger numbers in all areas to advise on prevention, diagnose disease and treat the sick. The quality of health care they provide greatly depends on the kind of training they receive; on the opportunities they have of continuing to learn higher standards from others; on their willingness to work as members of a health team in rural health centres, clinics and hospitals.

In the proposals we put forward for health expenditures in the future, a large part of it is educational in nature. In this sense, the Treasury must come to regard the Health Estimates as containing a substantial element of spending on education. This element is composed of three parts: the recruitment and training of new workers; the allocation of more of the time of the highly trained to supervising and improving the work of auxiliary grades; the allocation of more of the time of all members of the health team to preventive community medicine. This means, as we have already said, passing on to the people the technical lessons of health education, nutrition, food preparation, germ infection, child care and home economics in general.

These objectives call, during the next seven or eight years for a 'crash' programme of training three major categories of health workers; medical practitioners, medical aids and maternity aids. In terms of numbers and cost, these—along with nurses—are the most important training needs of the 1960s. Our plan requires, towards the end of a twenty-year period of development, three times the present number of doctors, five times the number of medical aids, an increase of 50% in the number of nurses, the training of 2,000 maternity aids—a new category of health worker—and substantial increases in other categories of auxiliary, technical and administrative staff.

We do not think that henceforward Tanganyika should rely wholly on training programmes outside its own borders to provide medical practitioners to serve its nine million people in the rural areas. Thus, we regard as highly important the new course for medical practitioners which will, we hope, be inaugurated this year. Its development, as a pioneering experiment in training doctors to meet the needs of the Tanganyikan people, will be watched by leaders of medical policy in many other countries. But until these new doctors have emerged in considerable numbers from the training school in Dar es Salaam, it will be necessary greatly to expand as quickly as possible the training of medical aids, and to start new courses for maternity aids and other categories of medical and social welfare workers as outlined in Chapter 9. Thereafter, the annual output of newly trained medical aids should be reduced somewhat, but these and other categories of health workers will be permanently required to staff a steadily expanding health service.

In addition to these programmes, it will be necessary to look to Makerere for more medical staff to man the hospitals and other sectors of the health service. There will also be a continuing need for foreign doctors. But these, by and large, will be required as specialists and not as general medical practitioners—specialists in the different clinical and surgical branches of medicine, experienced medical administrators, technical advisers and research workers.

These are the main requirements for staff to provide services at different kinds of institutions distributed more evenly over the whole of the country. We recommend the establishment of 200 health centres, generously staffed for supervisory and health education purposes, and 1,000 health clinics to act as their outposts. These centres and clinics will be the front-line of medical care. They will be supported by area and regional supervisory staff and by twenty-six area hospitals (all of which must have at least 200 beds and five doctors) and three national reference hospitals of over 500 beds staffed by specialists. All these hospitals should be reserved for those patients whose medical needs can only be met by hospital care.

In our plans for the hospital services we decided to give priority to quality rather than to quantity. As a whole, we are proposing fewer but larger hospitals providing a much higher standard of in-patient care. Counting the supervised beds in health centres along with all hospital beds with resident medical staff we are, in fact, recommending an increase of some 20% in the absolute number of medically supervised beds. In terms, however, of beds per 1,000 population this will mean a reduction if the population increases substantially by 1980. This decline in the relative amount of provision is, however, necessary to improve the quality of the hospital services and to give the highest priority to developing the rural and preventive health services within a limited health budget. If the rate of population growth slows down substantially over the next twenty years, there will be no reduction in the number of medically supervised beds per head.

Should our proposals be accepted by the Government and by all concerned with the health of the people they will represent a great challenge for the next two decades. Tanganyika will be attempting to do in a relatively short period what more developed societies only achieved after a much longer period of trial and struggle. What we are recommending cannot happen in a season; many changes will be needed which, inevitably, cannot benefit everyone alike. Some will be asked to make sacrifices; others to show goodwill and toleration. Those, for example, who have access to the best medical care will be expected to pay more of the cost if they are able to do so. Newly trained doctors will be asked to serve a period of national professional service. Established private practitioners, if granted monopoly rights in some urban areas, may be called on to make a financial contribution (this proposal is supported by only some members of the Survey Committee). Civil servants will be required to relinquish their privileged position of recipients of free medical care. Voluntary agencies will be expected to collaborate to a far greater extent with each other and with the Ministry of Health. Local authorities will have to hand over their responsibilities for personal health services to the central government. Employers may be required to contribute to a new health insurance scheme for workers in designated areas. The people themselves will be asked to make their own voluntary contribution towards better health through participation in the activities of self-help and community development.

Given these things, given the continuation of national self-discipline, we believe that our plan for a unified health service can be translated into fact. The pace of development will, of course, depend upon many economic and social factors which we are unable to predict. Above all, it will depend on the rate of population growth. If another five million Tanganyikans—and mostly young Tanganyikans— have to be provided with health services by 1980, a doubling of expenditure by that year will allow much less room for improvement in the standard of health services than if the population increases more slowly. We believe, therefore, that the government should give the most serious attention to the need for launching another educational campaign. The people have a right to know that, if they so wish, they can limit the size of their families. They can choose to have smaller, healthier and better fed families. They can choose to have better educated children or uneducated children. They can decide the future of Ujamaa. These are among the many decisions that Tanganyikans will have to make about the welfare of their families, their fellows and their country in the years ahead.

12 Summary of Principal Recommendations

The main emphasis in our recommendations is on the need for the balanced development of the health services within an overall national plan. We stress the need for closer integration of services provided by central government, local government and voluntary agencies and for separate though co-ordinated provision for personal and environmental services. Implicit in our recommendations is a radical shift of emphasis from curative to preventive medicine and to the development of services specially adapted to the needs and resources of Tanganyika.

We have tried to look forward as far as 1980. In doing so, we were compelled to make certain assumptions about the resources likely to be available for the development of health services and about future population trends.

In considering the probable level of expenditure, we assumed that there would be no radical change in the proportion of government spending devoted to health services. Nevertheless, given a satisfactory rate of increase of the national income, we felt justified in assuming an annual increase of 4% in health expenditure. Our recommendations are, therefore, based on an assumed rate of expenditure of about £7 m. per annum on current account by 1980 and £1 m. per annum on capital expenditure (pp. 84-89). It seemed wise to allow for the possibility of a rate of increase of population being larger than previously envisaged. The rate of growth might reach 3% per annum before 1980. We have assumed throughout this Report a total population of about 15 million by 1980 (pp. 90-97). This would represent an increase of about 50% over the present total population and an increase in expenditure per head from about seven shillings to about ten shillings. A slower rate of population growth, or a more rapid increase in expenditure, would permit the targets we have proposed for 1980 to be reached somewhat earlier.

The principal recommendations embodied in earlier chapters are as follows:

Health Areas

1. The country should be divided into forty health areas, each containing an average of five health centres and twenty-five health clinics. The number of areas should be increased as finance and trained staff become available (pp. 108-9, 115, 118).

2. Eventually each health area should have its own general hospital. The immediate aim should be to provide a total of twenty-nine general hospitals, eleven of which will serve two health areas each (p. 109).

3. The health area headquarters staff should include three medical practitioners, two nursing staff, two medical aids, a mental welfare assistant and an administrative assistant (p. 116).

4. The area headquarters should be located in a town health centre, preferably near the area hospital but not under its control (p. 108).

5. The main functions of the area team should be to provide leadership and supervision for the 'health units' (a health centre and its satellite clinics) and technical guidance for the environmental services in its area. Supervision should be regarded as primarily an educational process (pp. 116-17).

6. Adequate means of communication are essential between area headquarters, health centres and hospitals. Where neither telephone nor telegraph facilities exist, radio communications should be established (p. 115).

Health Units

1. The principal objectives of our recommendations re-

garding local personal health services are stated in Chapter 5, as follows:

> 'to give to the rural population a better medical service;
>
> —to infuse into these local services a preventive approach;
>
> —to provide a continuous system of supervision of the staff and health education of the public;
>
> —to link closely the work of these services and the movement for self-help and community development, and
>
> —to protect the hospitals and so enable them to perform their special and particular functions.'
> (pp. 106-7).

Thus we recommend the establishment of a network of health centres and health clinics. Some of the existing dispensaries and small hospitals might be adapted for these purposes (p. 114).

2. There should be a branch of the health services within walking distance of most of the population. Our plan assumes that initially in sparsely populated areas each health unit will be serving about 50,000 people and in densely populated areas they will be serving up to 100,000 people (pp. 108-9).

3. The local personal health services should be owned and operated by the central government to which existing local authority facilities should be transferred. The voluntary agencies should be asked to withdraw gradually from this field of activity (p. 147).

4. The main functions of the health centre staff should be to provide

   (i) supervision, training and leadership for the local health clinics (p. 107).

   (ii) clinical care of a high standard and a system of referral to hospital where necessary (p. 107).

   (iii) a permanent base for campaigns against endemic and epidemic diseases (pp. 102, 112).

5. The staff of a health centre should include one medical practitioner as director, one senior medical aid as

deputy director, two medical aids, three nurses, two maternity aids and one nursing orderly. In the early years, public health staff should also be attached to rural health centres. We recommend, however, that the environmental health services should be the responsibility of the local authorities (p. 168).

6. Each health centre should have a number of maternity beds for patients requiring observation and 'holding' beds for illnesses of short duration and patients awaiting transfer to hospital (p. 112).

7. The director of the health centre and his staff nurse should visit each health clinic at least fortnightly, and undertake part of the regular work of the clinic in addition to dealing with difficult cases, thus helping to raise the standards of the medical and maternity aids on the staff of the clinics (p. 111).

8. The functions of the health centre director should include, in addition to his clinical duties, the study of local conditions, the organization of preventive measures, the collection of statistics, and co-operation with other local agencies as expert adviser on health needs (pp. 112-3).

9. A motor vehicle should be attached to each health centre, to be used mainly for transporting staff but also, in emergencies, as an ambulance (p. 127).

10. One health centre should be used as a 'staff college' for training senior health unit staff (p. 199).

11. The staff of a health clinic should include one medical aid, one maternity aid and one nursing orderly (pp. 110-11). Sufficient staff should be available for health clinics so that by 1970 no dispensary, in the charge of a tribal dresser, will remain (p. 192).

12. The main functions of the health clinic staff should be

   (i) treating minor ailments and infections and referring patients to the health centre or hospital when necessary;

   (ii) maternity and child care work, including prenatal examinations and regular examination of older children;

   (iii) participation in immunization and health

education campaigns organized from the health centre (p. 110).

13. The health clinics should maintain a high standard of hygiene as an example to the local community and should carry adequate stocks of drugs for the treatment of acute infections (p. 111).

General hospitals

1. The hospitals should admit only those patients who cannot be properly cared for elsewhere. Except in emergencies, all patients should be referred by a doctor outside the hospital (pp. 106, 119).

2. There should be fewer hospitals, but each should have at least 200 beds, five doctors and a properly staffed X-ray unit and pathological laboratory. No more small hospitals should be built (pp. 106, 119).

3. There should be two categories of hospitals, 'A' hospitals with over 500 beds, specialist staff and post-graduate training facilities; and 'B' hospitals with 200-250 beds. By 1980 there should be three 'A' hospitals, including the Princess Margaret Hospital, Mwanza Hospital (greatly expanded) and a third probably in the north of the country; and twenty-six 'B' hospitals. Altogether these will provide 8,000 beds, or one per 1,875 of the assumed population. Each of these hospitals will serve one or more health areas (pp. 123-4, 127-9).

4. Some of the voluntary agency hospitals should be designated as 'B' hospitals, subject to the revised system of government grants described in Chapter 7 (and see below). Others might be reorganized and designated as health centres or clinics in the government service (pp. 122-4).

5. Consideration should be given to the idea of a central sterile supply service (already adopted at the Princess Margaret Hospital), the use of disposable equipment, and the advantages of good building design in reducing dirt and cleaning costs (p. 127).

6. The principle of 'progressive patient care' should be

introduced where the layout of hospital buildings permits, or where major alterations or new buildings are undertaken (pp. 126-7).

7. Some of the work of the hospitals at present undertaken by medical assistants will eventually fall upon senior medical aids. They will not, however, be able to undertake work which would normally be done by qualified doctors (p. 126).

8. Lay hospital administrators should be used to relieve medical and nursing staff of administrative and clerical duties (p. 125).

9. General hospitals should act as ambulance stations for their areas (p. 127).

10. 'A' hospitals should provide pre-registration training for newly qualified doctors, and registrarships and clinical assistantships, for which doctors who have worked for a period in a 'B' hospital should be eligible. They should be training centres for nurses and technicians of various kinds (pp. 129-130).

11. Consultants from 'A' hospitals should visit 'B' hospitals for consultation, advice and teaching (p. 129).

12. 'B' hospitals should set professional standards for the health units in their areas and act as 'postgraduate' centres for health unit staffs. Some of them should provide pre-registration training for newly qualified doctors (p. 124).

13. For government hospitals Advisory Committees should gradually be established, as a means of coordinating area health services and providing opportunities for democratic participation in hospital management (p. 202).

Voluntary Agency Hospitals

1. The voluntary agencies should be encouraged to concentrate their medical activities on the provision of hospitals as an integral part of the national plan (p. 147).

2. A policy-making and executive body, representing the

227

grant-aided agencies—a Voluntary Agency Planning Committee—should be formed (p. 148).

3. A Consultative Committee should also be established to ensure that hospitals and other services provided by non-grant-aided bodies conform to the needs of the national plan (p. 148).

4. Government grants should be payable in respect of voluntary agency hospitals under either of two schemes.

Under Scheme I the government would assume financial responsibility for the hospital. It would be run by a Board of Management (representing the voluntary agency, the Ministry and the local authority and community development committees) which would be subject to the general policy directions of the Ministry. The Chairman of the Board would, however, be nominated by the voluntary agency, in order to preserve the religious character and traditions of the institution. Scheme II broadly follows existing arrangements, except that bed grants would be withdrawn over a period of three years; and a number of new conditions would be laid down, principally :

(i) establishment of an Advisory Committee (similar in composition to the Board of Management in Scheme I);

(ii) payment of government basic salary and wage scales;

(iii) imposition of the charges for in-patient and out-patient treatment recommended in Chapter 7.

Agencies which cannot afford to provide a service of the standard required under Scheme II might be able to participate under Scheme I. These changes would have to be introduced gradually and revised as circumstances alter (pp. 149-54).

5. The Minister would have the right to withhold or withdraw grants on the grounds that

(i) the conditions are not being fulfilled;

(ii) religious discrimination is practised or patients are obliged to receive religious instruction;

      (iii) training bodies' regulations and syllabuses are not complied with, or

      (iv) prescribed records are not kept or returns are not submitted (p. 154).

6. Where voluntary hospitals no longer qualify for grant aid, the grants should be withdrawn gradually over a period of five years (p. 147).

Special Hospitals

1. The trend should be towards specialized departments or units in general hospitals rather than separate hospitals (p. 131).

2. Tuberculosis patients should, in general, be treated in special units of the general hospital with suitable accommodation and staffing arrangements for outpatient treatment and supervision in association with health units. Kibongoto Hospital should continue to serve the Kilimanjaro area and as a national centre for tuberculosis research (pp. 132-3).

3. The leprosy hospitals should in future be used only to provide institutional care for severely disabled patients (p. 132).

4. At least one more mental hospital is needed, in addition to psychiatric and 'holding' units in general hospitals. Dar es Salaam seems the obvious place for the new hospital (pp. 133-5).

5. The mental hospitals should offer postgraduate training, and all medical staff should be encouraged to spend a period at one of them (pp. 134, 136).

6. Trained mental nursing staff and mental welfare officers will be required to work in conjunction with the psychiatric holding units (p. 134).

7. Chiefs and police should be required to bring people awaiting certification to the nearest medical unit or (if necessary) hospital as soon as possible and the practice of putting them in prison abolished as soon as possible (pp. 133-4).

8. Medical practitioners should receive instruction in mental health and disease so that treatment of mental

cases can be provided at health centres and general hospitals (p. 134).

Charges for Medical Care
Charges for certain forms of medical care should be introduced when adequate systems of referral have been organized (pp. 155-64).

Out-patients:
1. Charges should be regarded as a means of directing demand for first consultation to the peripheral sectors of the health services and encouraging a system of referral (pp. 159-61).
2. Charges, where imposed, should be modest and one charge should give the right to free medicine and re-attendance for up to four weeks, and longer in certain cases (p. 160).
3. No charges should be made in any unit smaller than a health centre (health clinics and dispensaries) in order to provide free initial consultation and simple treatment near the patients' homes (p. 161).
4. The charge for first consultation by appointment at a hospital should be considerably higher than the charge at a health centre. But no charge should be made at hospitals for out-patients referred from health centres (pp. 161-2).
5. No charges should be made at health centres or hospitals for children under school leaving age and for expectant and nursing mothers referred from health clinics and centres (p. 161).
6. The person in charge of the unit should be entitled to waive charges for emergency cases and for 'indigents' (p. 161).
7. There should be no exemption from charges for government employees (p. 162).

In-patients:
8. There should be no charge for in-patient treatment at a health centre, except in the case of normal confinements (p. 162).

9. A uniform, modest, daily charge should be made for hospital in-patients, with a substantially higher charge for normal confinements. Those exempt from any charge would be children, abnormal confinements, 'indigents' and patients suffering from mental illness and certain specified communicable diseases (p. 162).
10. Charges for amenity beds should be considerably higher; these charges should vary according to the amenity available; there should be no variation in the quality of medical and nursing care provided (p. 163).

Environmental Health Services
1. Eventually the responsibility for environmental health services should fall upon the local authorities (pp. 142, 168-69).
2. Local authorities should be required to form public health committees and to enact and administer bye-laws (p. 142). Model bye-laws should be provided (pp. 173-4).
3. The staff of the health inspectorate should be transferred to the local authorities when an appropriate committee has been formed and legislation prepared. An initial target should be to have at least one health inspector to each Council (pp. 142, 174).
4. The Ministry of Health should provide technical advice and supervision through regional and area health officers (p. 174).
5. Technical assistance and grants to local authorities for capital works should be made available by the central government, whose approval should be obtained before such works are undertaken (p. 174).
6. A new survey of sanitary conditions in Dar es Salaam, Tanga and the larger towns should be carried out (p. 168).
7. Town planning, the encouragement of a social structure favourable to family and community life, and community development self-help schemes should be used to mitigate the undesirable consequences of urban growth (p. 171).

8. Health regulations for estates and mines should be revised, distinguishing between general obligations and those relating to particular types of employment. Employers should be fully responsible for prevention and arrangements for treatment of disease or injury arising out of employment (pp. 174-5).

Recruitment and Training

1. Over the next twenty years, the number of qualified staff employed in the government and associated voluntary services should increase as follows (all figures are approximate):
   (i) Medical practitioners from 250 to 750;
   (ii) Medical aids from 400 to 2,000;
   (iii) Nurses from 1,500 to 2,250;
   (iv) Maternity aids (new grade) to 2,000 (p. 179).
2. The training of medical staff should stress the needs of rural areas, through practical work in the field. This is especially important in view of the inevitable concentration of training facilities in Dar es Salaam (p. 205).
3. A new programme for training medical practitioners in Tanganyika is recommended. It is recommended that they should be enrolled on the same register as medical practitioners trained elsewhere. Although most of them would work in the health centres, they should be eligible for hospital posts (pp. 125-6, 184-8, 246-9).
4. The training course for Tanganyika medical practitioners should start in 1963 with twenty-five students, the annual entry to increase to fifty when facilities permit. It should be open to applicants with School Certificate or GCE 'O' level in appropriate subjects. The course should last four years, followed by a two-year pre-registration period (pp. 185, 188).
5. A Board of Governors for the training school for medical practitioners and other staff should be set up. Its members should include representatives of the Ministry of Health, the Department of Education, the

University of East Africa and the Technical College of Dar es Salaam. The Governors should appoint a full-time principal. Through a series of 'course committees' he would be responsible for all the courses for medical practitioners and assistant grades of staff, and for approving posts in hospitals and health centres for pre-registration posts. A lay bursar should also be appointed who would be responsible for the facilities of the school, including residential accommodation (pp. 205-6).

6. During the transition period of the 1960s, before adequate numbers of medical practitioners are available, it is recommended that the supply of trained medical aids should be expanded as quickly as possible (pp. 188-9).

7. The number of medical aids in training should be temporarily increased to 200 a year. Newly-trained medical aids should work under supervision at a health centre before taking charge of a health clinic (pp. 191-3).

8. Post-qualification training programmes for medical aids should be started within three years, to fit them for posts as senior medical aids in health centres and hospitals (p. 192).

9. The training of maternity aids should be on the lines of the recently abandoned health nurses' course, but with more emphasis on midwifery. The course should last two years and entrants should have Standard VIII education. Married women should be encouraged to apply (p. 195).

10. The training of health orderlies should be systematized, standard of entry and duration of training being laid down. Training should be conducted on the job, but a national examination should be introduced (p. 197).

11. Other grades of staff in which expansion is needed include laboratory and radiography technicians and assistants, pharmacy assistants and dental assistants (p. 179).

12. There is a need for more psychiatric staff to work both in the mental hospitals and outside. More psychiatrists

are needed; a cadre of mental welfare assistants should be formed (selected students should be trained in the United Kingdom, but later possibly at Makerere); mental nursing should be introduced as an option for females in the nurse training course, and a special course in mental nursing should be arranged with the help of the nurses now being trained in the United Kingdom (pp. 135, 197-8).

13. To reduce staff changes, a system of appointment by means of advertisement and application at regional level should be substituted where possible for the existing system of 'posting' (p. 212).

14. Certain designated areas should be closed to new entrants to private practice. In return for the monopoly situation thus created, practitioners in private practice in those areas might be required to make a financial contribution to the government medical services. (Only some members of the Survey Committee supported this recommendation) (pp. 190-1).

15. The registers of medical practitioners and other categories of trained staff should be kept up to date annually, and those on these registers should be required to provide certain specified information (p. 190).

Population Statistics and Family Planning

1. Estimates of population and trends in fertility and mortality should be ascertained (on a sample basis if appropriate) at least every five years (p. 97).

2. The registration of births and deaths should be introduced gradually by areas. This should be the responsibility of a Registrar General (p. 209).

3. Information and facilities for the voluntary practice of family planning should be made available, after a 'prelimitation phase' of education and investigation of beliefs and values (pp. 95-7).

Health Insurance

1. The development of a system of health insurance is envisaged. It is recommended that this should be in-

troduced gradually for employed persons in designated areas (pp. 164-7).

National Headquarters and Regional Organization

1. The Chief Medical Officer might find it useful to act through three deputies, responsible for preventive, curative and training services respectively (p. 204).
2. A central epidemiological division should be established, directed by a trained epidemiologist, to collect and analyse data, undertake surveys, anticipate new trends and needs and to advise on control measures (pp. 207-9).
3. The existing special units should remain separate (pp. 208-9).
4. In order to enlarge the activities of the nutrition unit, staff should be sent for training in survey methods (p. 210).
5. The pathology laboratory service should be developed to provide both a clinical diagnostic service for the hospitals and public health and forensic laboratory services for each region (p. 210).
6. A medical officer from the health education unit might be seconded to the Ministry responsible for community development (p. 211).
7. Regional offices under the direction of regional medical officers, should supervise and co-ordinate the work of hospitals, health units and local authorities in each region, as well as dealing with certain routine administrative tasks (pp. 202-3).
8. In each region a deputy regional medical officer should be appointed, to be exclusively concerned with environmental services (p. 203).
9. The form of financial accounts should be revised to provide a simple functional breakdown of both estimates and appropriations (pp. 211-12).

Appendix A

Organizational Chart of Proposed Health Services

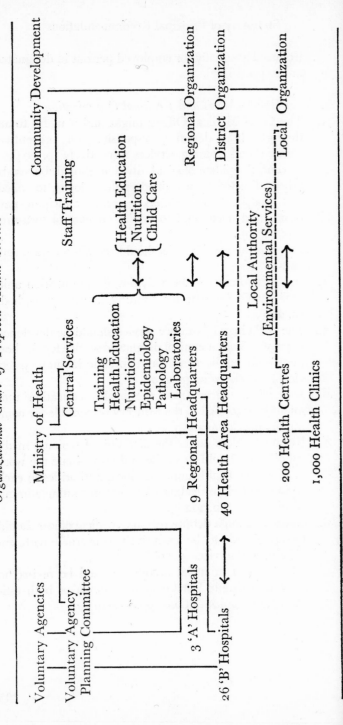

Appendix B. The Current Cost
of our Recommendations.

In this Appendix an attempt is made to estimate the cost of implementing our recommendations. To arrive at such calculations it has been necessary to make very detailed assumptions about the staff required and about other expenditures. These figures should not be interpreted as recommended budgets or as recommended establishments for the various parts of the health services. Nevertheless, we hope that the figures we have used do serve to indicate the order of magnitude of the annual current cost involved.

Before presenting our estimates, we attempt in Table I a more detailed division of the combined expenditures of central government, local government and the voluntary agencies than that shown in Chapter 2. The categories used in this Appendix follow the principal chapter headings of the Report so that comparisons can be made between the distribution of expenditure under the existing services and under our proposals. Inevitably, the figures given contain a very substantial element of guesswork.

Local Personal Health Services
In Tables II, III and IV we show estimates of the cost of the forty area headquarters, the 200 health centres and the 1,000 health clinics respectively in 1980.

Table I

A Classification of the Combined Current Expenditure of Central Government, Local Government and the Voluntary Agencies in 1961

	£'s	Totals
Local Personal Services		
Expenditure by central government hospital and outpatients' services . .	180,000*	
Expenditure by local government . .	650,000*	
Expenditure by voluntary agencies . .	100,000*	
		£930,000
Hospital Services		
Expenditure by central government		
Dar es Salaam	353,000*	
Pathological services	58,000	
Regional hospitals . . .	950,000*	
Mental hospitals	79,000	
Special hospitals	47,000	
Other	40,000	
Grants to voluntary agencies . . .	160,000	
Expenditure by voluntary agencies (net expenditure	590,000*	
		£2,277,000
Environmental Services		
Expenditure by central government. .	80,000*	
Expenditure by local government .	100,000*	
		£180,000
Other Services		
Expenditure by central government		
Teaching and research . .	40,000	
Regional offices	50,000*	
Headquarters and central services . .	160,000	
		£250,000
	Total:	£3,637,000†

*These figures in particular involve a substantial element of guess-work.

†It is estimated that approximately £650,000 is spent by central and local government and the voluntary agencies on capital projects e.g. Table X, p. 68

Appendix B

Table II

Area Headquarters (40)

Staff per unit	Grade	Total needed under the proposals	Average Salary £	Total Cost £
1	Area Health Officer .	40	1,482	59,280
2	Medical Practitioners	80	1,062	84,960
1	Sister . .	40	720	28,800
1	Mental Welfare Asst.	40	516	20,640
1	Administrative Asst. . .	40	516	20,640
1	Nurse 'A' .	40	255	10,200
2	Medical Aids .	80	201	16,080
1	Clerk . .	40	139	5,560
2	Drivers .	80	86	6,880
4	Subordinates .	160	60	9,600
			Total:	£262,640

Other Costs			Each H.Q. £	
Transport (2 vehicles) . .			4,500	180,000
Rent, light, heat, stationery, uniforms etc. . . .			420	16,800
			Total:	£459,440

Table III
Health Centres (200)

Staff per centre	Grade	Total needed under the proposals	Average Salary £	Total Cost £
1	Medical Practitioner .	200	1,062	212,400
1	Senior medical aid . .	200	255	51,000
1	Nurse 'A' .	200	255	51,000
2	Medical aids .	400	201	80,400
2	Nurse 'B' .	400	201	80,400
2	Maternity aids	400	201	80,400
1	Nursing orderly	200	117	23,400
1	Driver . .	200	86	17,200
5	Subordinate staff (cleaners, laundry) .	1,000	60	60,000
			Total:	£656,200

		Each centre £	
Other Costs			
Drugs and dressings . .		2,000	400,000
Transport		1,350	270,000
Maintenance of buildings .		250	50,000
Uniforms, linen, radios etc. .		200	40,000
	Total:		£1,416,200

Appendix B

Table IV

Health Clinics (1,000)

Staff per clinic	Grade	Total needed under the proposals	Average Salary £	Total Cost £
1	Medical aid .	1,000	201	201,000
1	Maternity aid.	1,000	201	201,000
1	Nursing orderly	1,000	117	117,000
2	Subordinates .	2,000	60	120,000
			Total:	£639,000

Other Costs			Cost per clinic	
Drugs and dressings	.	.	300	300,000
Other .	.	.	.	.	50	50,000
			Total:	£989,000

Thus, in total, the local personal health services will cost about £2·9 million per annum, consisting of about £500,000 for the area headquarters, about £1·4 million for the health centres, and about £1,000,000 for the health clinics.

Hospital Services

In Table V we estimate the cost of a 'B' hospital.

Table V

'B' Hospitals (26)

Number	Grade	Salary	Cost per Hospital
Administrative		£	£
1	Hospital Secretary (Ex.4) . .	900	900
1	Assistant Secretary (Ex.3) . .	732	732
2	Administrative Assistants (Ex.2).	516	1,032
2	Record Clerks . . .	375	750
5	Clerks (C.O.1.) . . .	201	1,005
			4,419
Nursing			
1	Matron (T.O.4) . . .	900	900
12	Sisters (T.O.3) . . .	720	8,640
1	Housekeeper (Ex.2) . . .	516	516
12	Senior Staff Nurses (T.O.2) .	516	6,192
24	Staff Nurses (T.O.1) . .	255	6,120
27	Nursing Orderlies (S.C.2) .	117	3,159
12	Domestics	60	720
			26,247
Medical			
1	Medical Superintendent (A.P.3 B)	1,482	1,482
3	Medical Officers (A.P.2) . .	1,062	3,186
1	Registrar	1,038	1,038
1	Assistant Medical Officer (T.O.4)	900	900
1	Assistant Dental Officer (T.O.4).	900	900
2	Medical Assistants (T.O.1.A) .	345	690
2	Senior Medical Aids (T.O.1.) .	255	510
			8,706

Table V. '*B*' *Hospitals* (26)—*continued*

Number	Grade	Salary	Cost per Hospital
Technical		£	£
1	Senior Laboratory Technician (T.O.3)	720	720
2	Laboratory Technicians (T.O.2).	516	1,032
2	Laboratory Assistants (T.O.1) .	255	510
3	Laboratory Auxiliaries (M.T.) .	201	603
1	Pharmacist (T.O.3) . . .	720	720
1	Pharmacist Assistant (T.O.1) .	255	255
1	Radiographer (T.O.3) . .	720	720
1	Radiographic Assistant (M.T.) .	201	201
1	Physiotherapist (T.O.3) . .	720	720
1	Social Worker (T.O.2) . .	516	516
			5,997
Other			
1	Cook (Ex.2)	516	516
3	Telephone Operators (S.C.3) .	162	486
3	Drivers (S.C.1) . . .	86	258
1	Head Porter (M.T.) . . .	201	201
15	Auxiliary staff (S.C.1) . .	86	1,290
40	Subordinates (–) . . .	60	2,400
			5,151
	Total Staff:		£50,520
Other Expenditure			
	Provisions (2/- per patient per day) .		8,212
	Drugs and Dressings		10,000
	Ambulance Running Costs (2 Vehicles)		10,000
	Maintenance of buildings, linen, equipment etc.		10,000
	Total Expenditure:		£88,732

Each 'B' hospital will cost nearly £89,000. Thus, twenty-six such hospitals will cost about £2·3 million per annum. We have not attempted to work out detailed establishments and budgets of the three 'A' hospitals. We have simply assumed that on average each hospital will cost slightly less than the whole Dar es Salaam complex with its 750 beds. On this basis we estimate that the 'A' hospitals will amount in total to a cost of about £900,000 per annum. Similarly, we have taken the cost of the two mental hospitals to be about £200,000 which is more than three times the cost of the existing hospitals at Dodoma. Allowing a further £150,000 for special hospitals and centralized pathological services, we estimate that the total cost of hospital services will be about £3·6 million per annum.

Table VI

Combined Current Expenditure of Central Government, Local Government and Voluntary Agencies in 1961 and under our proposals

	1961 £. million	Proposed Health Services £. million	Percentage change
Local Personal Health Services .	0·9	2·9	+208%
Hospital Services .	2·3	3·6	+ 58%
Environmental Services . .	0·2	0·5	+178%
Other. . .	0.3	0·5	+100%
Total:	3·6	7·5	

The totals and the percentages have been calculated on unrounded figures.

Appendix B

Environmental and Other Services

We guess that about £500,000 per annum will be required for the environmental service, and about £500,000 for other services.

On the foregoing basis and assumptions it is possible to compare in Table VI current expenditure in 1961 with that envisaged under our proposals.

The greatest expansion is in the local personal health services and the environmental services. The expansion of expenditure on the hospital services is relatively modest.

Appendix C. Outline of Proposed New Curriculum for Tanganyika-Trained Practitioners.

It is recommended that the curriculum should be designed basically as a vocational training for those who will work in the new health centres. Throughout, the students' interest should be focused on the type of community he will ultimately serve and the facilities likely to be available. The orientation of the curriculum to general practice with emphasis on the social and preventive aspect of medicine is not intended to prevent those whose inclinations, aptitudes and subsequent training fit them for appointments in hospitals or other fields of medicine from following such careers.

We endorse the opinion of the WHO Study Group report on internationally acceptable minimum standards of medical education that a medical education 'requires not only a certain store of factual information but also the development of an attitude of mind ready to accept the new and to abandon, or amend, the old. It is only by having such a critical outlook that the physician will be able to adapt himself to the future, about which the only thing certain is that it will be different. The Group believed strongly that a satisfactory educational system must be based on the principle of learning by experience and a measure of self-education. It is necessary, therefore, to use the minimum of didactic teaching and instruction, whether in the lecture theatre or in the hospital, of the sort that precludes active participation by the students. Emphasis should be placed on practical laboratory work, active supervised participation in the investigation and treatment of patients, and free discussion between

master and pupil.'[1] We would stress here again the importance we attach to frequent and continued active association
of students in the work of rural health centres, such as the
new demonstration health centre being established by the
Nordic Mission twelve miles from Dar es Salaam and the
special training centre at Ifakara provided by the Basle
Tropical Institute.

The proposed curriculum (not set out in detail here) is
essentially based on the principles behind the four-year
course of pre-clinical and clinical studies developed at
Western Reserve University in the United States. In general,
the curriculum is based on the study of biology and other
subjects which are introduced early and progressively elaborated with as little as possible fractionation into isolated
disciplines. The basis of the first year is biology and general
physiology including elementary biochemistry, taught first
with reference to the mammal, with some mammalian dissection, in parallel with teaching on cellular biology and
basic histology. It proceeds then to human anatomy and
physiology, the two subjects being taught together in relation to the cardiovascular, respiratory and other systems and
on a basis of foetal dissection. It proceeds to the biology of
parasites, including helminths, protozoa, bacteria and in-
sects of medical importance. These complete the main body
of the first year, but there is in parallel to them an introduction to the work of later years in the form of epidemiology
and statistics, and family care, for which the student would
be assigned the responsibility of watching family health,
noting the growth of children and their welfare, and reporting all illness to the centre of clinic for further attention.

The second year consists basically of an elaboration of
anatomy, physiology, and biochemistry, including the study
of adult dissection material (possibly prepared at Makerere)
nutrition and pathology. Pathology would start on the basis
of cellular and tissue changes following infection, ischaemia,
trauma, influence by chemical agents or other abnormality,
and would proceed to a study of pathology by systems. It

[1] World Health Organization. *Internationally Acceptable Minimum Standards
of Medical Education*. Technical Report 239 (Geneva, 1962), p. 26.

would be very desirable that this should follow naturally from the previous study of anatomy and physiology by systems and the histology and cellular pathology might with advantage be taught by the same individual. In parallel with these subjects there would be instruction in physical diagnostic methods, and the student would attend out-patient clinics of two types: routine clinics concerned largely with recognition and measurement of the normal and differentiation of the abnormal; that is, ante- and post-natal, infant and child welfare clinics; and for the second half of the year he would participate for one full day per week in the work of a rural health centre.

The student would start the third year by three months' participation in the work of a health centre, with an epidemiological bias, where he would be resident. During this time he would participate in health centre practice, but there would be major emphasis on social, environmental and epidemiological studies, during which he would gain an acquaintance with the health aspects of social background, housing, water, food and wastes, when he might make a small, individual epidemiological study of the chain of transmission of a disease. This could be arranged, for instance, by the detection of a case of tuberculosis, the recognition of early cases in its neighbourhood, together with the techniques of following up both cases and contacts; or by identification of the transmission of malaria, bilharziasis, trypanosomiasis, filariasis or relapsing fever, together with their hosts. He would submit a personal study report on the subject. An excellent background for this training is now provided through the help of the Basle Tropical Institute, at Ifakara. We understand that the Basle Institute has agreed to continue this for some years, and hope that this or a comparable training centre will be continuously available.

He would proceed, though not necessarily consecutively, to a comparable environmental and social study lasting one month in an urban environment.

At the end of this period the student would start on his phase of clinical medicine and patient care, having already a sound background including a considerable introduction to clinical medicine and diagnostic methods. This phase would last twenty months and be divided between ward and out-patient work for medicine, surgery, gynaecology and paediatrics with regular attendance at autopsies, together with periods of supervised attachment to psychiatric and tuberculosis units, and regular attendance at a health centre. The psychological and cultural bases of illness, both physical and mental, will be emphasized by the teachers in all clinical subjects throughout the course. Obstetrics would be taught systematically and by assistance at ante- and postnatal clinics and confinements.

Examinations at intervals throughout the course are considered essential. We do not specify the type of examination, but the use of labour-saving multiple choice questions should be considered. It is essential that an external examiner should participate in the final examination.

INDEX

251

Index

Index

253

Index

Index

Index

Index

Medical Advisory Committee, 148

Medical Aid to the Developing Countries, 199

Medical aids, 25, 28, 103, 111, 113, 116, 179, 218, 223, 225

  further training, 105, 191, 192

  number of, 191, 232, 233

  post-qualification training, 192, 233

  training of, 11, 19, 61, 233

Medical assistant, 11, 24, 25, 26, 30, 40, 57, 58, 103, 227

  course extended to three years, 10

  duties of, 15

  number in 1962, 47

  recruiting of, 180 et seq.

  shortage of, 28

  training of, 6, 7, 19, 61, 205

Medical auxiliaries (*see* Medical aids)

Medical care, 157

  charges for, 155, 230

  lack of uniformity of charges for, 155

Medical Council of Tanganyika, 186

  functions of, 187

  licensing Tanganyika-trained medical practitioners, 187

Medical Grants-in-Aid Advisory Committee, 17

Medical Officer of Health, 4, 167, 176

Medical practitioners, 14, 25, 113, 116, 218, 223, 224, 233

  duties in rural areas, 105

  increase in numbers of, 232

  mental health instruction, 229

  new course for, 185-6

number of, 47, 179

posting of, 212-3

present five grades of, 180

register of, 234

Medical Practitioners and Dentists Ordinance, 71, 186

Medical Practitioners Register, 187, 234

Medical research, development of, 81

Medical services—

  Africans' experience of, 3

  staffing, 73-4

Medical staff, training of, 232

Medical stores assistant, educational standard required, 15

Mental health, 62, 133 et seq., 208

Mental health services, 197

Mental hospitals, 9, 44, 131 et seq., 229

Mental illness, 162, 207, 231

  hospital provision for, 42, 43

  number of central government beds, 44

Mental nursing, 194, 233-4

  extension of training in, 197-8

  staff, 229

Mental patients,

  additional illnesses, 43

  certification of, 134, 229

  grants for the maintenance of, 17

  handling of, 43, 229

Mental welfare assistant, 116, 223, 233

  training of, 198

Mental welfare officers, 229

Midwifery, extension of facilities, 82

Midwives—

  locally trained, 193

Index

Index

Port health, 52
Post-war development, plan for health services (1947), 15
Pre-eradication programmes, 101, 103
Preventable diseases, free care of, 160
Preventive medicine, decreasing role of, 100-1
Pridie, Sir Eric, 17 et seq., 101, 102
recommendations of, 18 et seq.
White Paper (1949), 155
Pridie Report, 23, 156
Princess Margaret Hospital, 20, 25, 28, 46, 124, 128, 130, 131, 193, 204, 226
accommodation offered, 41
central sterile supply service, 127, 226
cost of, 25
number of beds (1961), 40
nurse/midwife training course, 194
two training schools, 205
Princess Margaret Nursing Training School, 194
Princess Margaret Training College, 50, 199
new course for health inspectors, 197
Private dental practice, 71
Private hospitals, 71
Private practice, 180, 183
not allowed for Government doctors, 46
numbers engaged in, 69
undesirable practices, 69-70
Private practitioners, 183, 220
Psychiatric holding units, 133 et seq.
Psychiatric staff, 43
need for, 233
Psychiatric units, 229, 249
Psychiatry, 129

Public Health Engineer, duties of, 174
Public health laboratory, 210
Public health service—
medical branch, 2
sanitation branch, 2 et seq.
slow development of, 31

RABIES, 76
vaccination campaigns, 53
Radiographers, 130
Radiography technicians, 179, 233
Regional Health Inspector, 197
Regional Medical Officer of Health, 176
Regional medical officers—
principal responsibilities, 202-3
their position today, 38
Register of Medical Practitioners, 190
Register of Midwives, 29
Register of Nurses, 29
Registrar-General, 209, 234
Registration of births, 80, 81, 209, 234
Registration of deaths, 80, 81, 209, 234
Report on Community Development in Africa (1956), 211
Report on Home Economics in Africa (1962), 211
'Resting beds', 33
Retail Price Index of Goods Consumed by Wage Earners, 85
Rhodesia, 93, 145
Roundworm, prevalence of, 77
Royal Society Health Certificate in Public Health Inspection, 197
Rufiji project, 75

Index

Rural dispensaries—
number of, 15-16
quality of treatment, 16
Rural health centres, 56
development of, 30-31
staff of, 30
Rural health services, 57
Rural medical aids (*see* Medical aids)
Rural Medical Services Committee (1948), Report on Dispensaries, 16

SANITARY inspectors, 6, 21, 51, 196, 197
training of, 3-4, 197
Sanitation, 3, 50, 142, 172, 173
survey of conditions, 167, 168, 231
Scandinavian aid, 30
Schistosomiasis—
control of, 174
environmental campaigns against, 169
Secondary education, extension of, 29
Second Report on the World Health Situation, 87, 88
Second World War, 62, 99
health services for forces, internees, refugees etc., 13
restriction of work of health services, 13
Self-help, 55, 56, 60, 93, 100, 104, 140, 168, 211, 214, 215, 221, 224, 231
Sewa Haji Hospital—
training dispensers, 7
training hospital assistants, 15
training laboratory assistants, 11
Singida, 55
Sleeping sickness, 21, 93
campaign against, 2, 16, 21
control of, 53

epidemic, 5
officer, 38
Unit, 4, 52
Smallpox, 76
vaccination campaigns, 2, 53
Southern Sudan, 93
Spens, Teresa, 211
Statistical data—
lack of, 78
inadequacy of, 79-80
Statistical Office, 97
Stevens, Mrs Rosemary, x
Syphilis, campaign against, 5

TABORA, 1, 39
maternal and child welfare clinic, 8
trypanosomiasis service, 208
Tanga, 38, 50, 57, 69, 75, 128
examination of sanitary conditions, 168, 231
hospital at, 130
number of beds in, 40
Medical Officer of Health, 3
Tanganyika—
African population of, 90
age structure of population, 79
beginning of organized medical services, 1
British Civil Medical Service in, 2
chief developments required towards meeting health needs, 81-2
crude birth rate, 37
development of the health services of, 1 et seq.
doctors in 1914, 2
economic survey mission report, 85, 86
effects of world slump, 9
epidemics, 76
fee-charging systems, 156
First World War, 2

Index

Index